The Diary of a
Farm Apprentice

William Carter Swan
1909–10

William Carter Swan
(14 May 1891–22 November 1918)

The Diary of a Farm Apprentice

William Carter Swan
1909–10

Edited by

E.E. Swan

ALAN SUTTON
1984

Alan Sutton Publishing Limited
17a Brunswick Road
Gloucester GL1 1HG

First published 1984   .

Copyright © E.E. Swan 1984

British Library Cataloguing in Publication Data

Swan, William Carter
    The diary of a farm apprentice.
    1. Dial post Farm (West Sussex)
    I. Title   II. Swan, E. E.
    338,1'09422'64   S522.G7

    ISBN 0-86299-109-9

Typesetting and origination by
Alan Sutton Publishing Limited.
Photoset Bembo 10/11
Printed in Great Britain

ACKNOWLEDGEMENTS

The photographs of farm work are from the Garland Collection and are reproduced by permission of Mrs. P. Gill, County Archivist, West Sussex. I wish to thank Mrs. Gill and her staff for the friendly and generous help they have given me.

I am grateful to the Keeper of Printed Books, Bodleian Library for permission to reproduce a print from the O.S. 3rd edn Sheet 138.

I also wish to thank: Mrs. G. Ruffhead for supplying photographs of the Diarist and Hydehurst Farm; Mrs. M. Bennett for the loan of photographs of Dial Post House; Mrs. Kitty Solomons for typing the manuscript; and my wife Joan for the help and encouragement she has given.

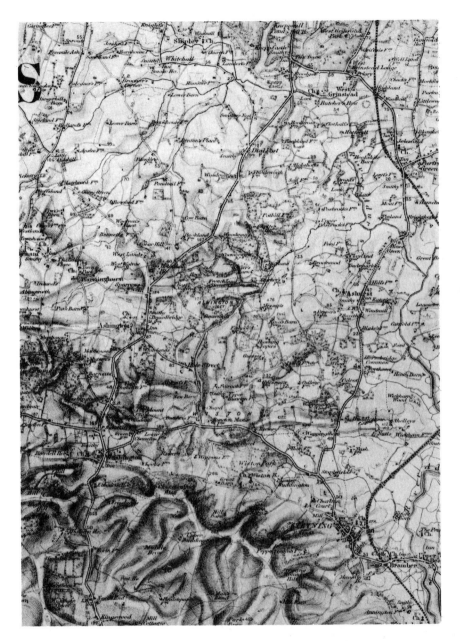

O.S. 3rd edition, a section of sheet 138

INTRODUCTION

.

This diary was kept by William Carter Swan when he was the farm apprentice of Mr. Venn of Dial Post Farm, Dial Post, Sussex, in the years 1909–10. He used pen and ink in a Boots Scribbling Diary interleaved with blotting paper, with a restricted space allocated to each day. He kept the diary primarily to help him when he acquired his own farm, so details of cultivations, sowing times and management of animals are frequent. He calls it 'a record of my apprenticeship and varied experiences', and these 'experiences' balance the farming detail.

He was home-sick, having left a close-knit family, and gradually he came to confide in the diary and his style developed confidence; personal feeling comes through when, for example, he asks the Governor for 'a little extra' for Sunday work, but 'tis no go, it seems rather hard'. Conditions of loneliness have always been conducive to good letter and diary writing. On 30 March 1910 he regrets the absence of a confidential friend and says how lonely he feels at times. Both the handwriting and style give the flavour of a world uninfluenced by jargon and the media. He had at his disposal an adequate vehicle for expressing what he wanted to say and, as in Bunyan, there are Biblical echoes; at lambing time he speaks of going after supper 'to take my watch over the flock'.

Will was the youngest of six children. His parents lived at Lucerne, a house on the outskirts of Slinfold, where his father – a carpenter who had founded a building business in London – had retired at the age of 50. Will was closest to his brother Sid who worked in the Worthing Post Office, but was to join Will farming on completion of the apprenticeship. Lucerne was a substantial house with adjoining paddock, where bees, 'Primrose' the cow, and a pony were kept.

Will liked to cycle home whenever possible, and sometimes even made the hour-long journey both ways after a hard day's work. Sunday followed a set pattern and Will would attend morning chapel, sometimes with the Venn family, at Billingshurst Mission Hall where he would usually meet his parents. Both families had a fundamentalist approach to religion, embodied in the flourishing Mission Halls and tin chapels of the period. Will embraced this faith in a sincere and uncritical way, although he was not above castigating a 'read' sermon. He relied on the Lord to

Will's parents and other members of the family

help him when faced with the extra responsibility of paying the men on Saturday night.

Will's apprenticeship with Mr. Venn was arranged through the freemasonry of the chapel, though the agreement drawn up by the two elders was none the less business-like for that, with a premium of £50, another £50 each year for board and lodging. Will received 2s. 6d. a week wages over the two years. Mr. Venn, unfortunately for a farmer, had five daughters and no son. He farmed 300 acres at Dial Post, plus an additional 112 acres at Rookland Farm which he took over at Michaelmas 1909. This was a large enterprise for one man to control and direct. The farmer was king in his own small self-contained world and farming hadn't substantially altered for hundreds of years. Will refers to Mr. Venn variously as 'the Boss', 'the Gov.', 'the Governor' – small wonder he was sometimes overworked and irascible, 'rather cross' was Will's euphemism.

It was a mixed farm with a milking herd of 100, pigs and sheep, and the all-important horse providing the power. The head carter was top man. Carters did not like to be away from the horses and were frequently being sent to the rail head at West Grinstead with their waggons for coal, cake, fertilizer, flints, slag, bricks, etc., as well as the daily milk cart to the station. The head carter, who had his boy to help him, was Hunt until, as Will records, 'he had a skirmish with the Governor' and left a fortnight later, to be succeeded by Gumbrell. On very rare occasions the carters were drafted for other work. On Thursday 7 July 1910, he wrote: 'To-day all hands, including carters go turning hay with rakes in Ten Acres and Burchells' – this after a long spell of wet weather and nearly spoilt hay. Other hands had their special skills, the Lucas brothers, referred to as Lucas and George, did the thatching, hedging and sowing with the seed barrow; George was also the shepherd. At any given time at least ten men were employed on the farm.

The retention of the old field names was necessary in order to direct the work, Crab Tree Croft, Thistly field, Nine Corners, Faggot Stack Meadow, Stock Park, and many more recur constantly and are still in use today. With so much stock to support, calves, heifers and bullocks as well as a milking herd and a flock of sheep, a lot of the farm was under the plough. It often seemed to be worked in small strips and pieces of only a few acres; these were under beans, turnips, swedes, mangold, cabbage, maize, trefolium and rye, as well as larger acreages under wheat and oats. Sheep were folded on the root crops and pitching a fold was a daily routine for Will, not having the labour-saving benefit of electric fencing. Some patches of sown arable were so small they could be 'cottoned' to keep the rooks off the seed. Hauling dung, ploughing, rolling, harrowing and drilling went on with monotonous regularity and by today's standards were very slow and labour-intensive. Weeding, pulling kilk (charlock), couching, and thistle spudding was all done by hand as was much of the hoeing, the latter making use of casual labour.

Dial Post House

Lucerne

Hydehurst Farm

Everything was on the human scale, and depended on the energy and muscle power of the individual labourer in the field. The dung carts, sometimes eight in number, moved almost toy-like from the cowyard to the mixen under the oak tree – nearer to Chaucer than to today's highly mechanized farming. Hay and corn harvest and the visits of the threshing tackle broke the monotony of cultivation and looking after the stock. They were times of heightened activity involving all hands except the cowmen. Given a good spell of weather, they worked till dark. Once Will, had to feed his sheep and pitch a fold by moonlight after a day's harvesting. No work, except the feeding of stock, was done on Sunday, however great the need to get the harvest in. Saturday was a full working day for the men (as were Bank Holidays) and they were given their orders at six-thirty each morning. The average weekly wage for a labourer in 1909 was around 18s., carters and cowmen getting 1s. 6d. above the basic rate.

Will's bicycle represented his freedom of movement and he spent much spare time mending punctures, which were frequent on the flint and dust roads. Once there was a cluster of pin pricks in the back tyre – sabotage, perhaps by one of the men who resented taking orders from the farm pupil. He bought a cyclometer and a bell, and spent evenings lacquering the frame. He taught Nellie, a Venn daughter, to ride and was given a pair of gloves for his pains. Cattle were driven along the roads to and from market and farm sales. Will took ten heifers to Haywards Heath market by road with an overnight stop at Bolney, using his bike and a dog. The only mention of a motor-car in the diary is when one was in collision with the milk cart, breaking its shafts. Frequent trains from West Grinstead enabled Mr. Venn to attend Horsham and Steyning markets on the same day. Communications and the pace of life was so much slower than today. The farmer could not pick up the telephone and make his arrangements for the day. Will had to be sent on his bicycle to book a truck at the Goods Yard for seventy-one sacks of wheat, or to deliver a bill. Moore, the carter, was sent to Portslade to collect a milling machine, and had to stop overnight on what, today, would be an hour's job in the Land Rover. Mr. Venn himself was very much on the move – visiting neighbours, scouring the country for the loan of a hay tedder, visiting Smithfield Show and the local markets, looking at farms for friends and making sure he had a bull at the right time to run with the heifers. The whole enterprise depended on his organizing ability.

Dial Post, though a small village, could at this time provide most of the services required by its farming inhabitants. Blacksmith, carpenter, sheep shearer, rabbiter, policeman, were all to hand. There were mills at both Partridge Green and Ashington and a timber yard nearby. Mr. Burgess kept the village shop where Will bought a pair of boots for 10s. 6d. and an overcoat for £2. He would sometimes go over to the Burgesses for a chat by their fire in the evening, on spiritual matters it was hinted, and found some of the questions difficult to answer.

'I hive the swarm'

Only two events of other than local interest are mentioned by Will: the death of Edward VII at 11.45 p.m. on Friday 6 May 1910 – 'the country is saddened by the death of its beloved King' – and M. Bleriot's first crossing of the Channel on Sunday 25 July 1909 in his monoplane.

The arrival of the steam-ploughing tackle at the farm on 4 May 1910 was a hint of mechanization to come. The horse had quite a time to go yet, but the agricultural revolution had begun. Will could not resist taking time off to have a look at the steam tackle working. Moore, the carter, 'waits on the steam tackle for water, etc.', and Gumbrell was sent to the station for steam coal to feed it. This particular steam-plough was the property of the estate that owned the farms, and was lent out to them.

The daily weather report soon became a feature of the entries, the reality of mud and muck taking over from the earlier more lofty intention of ending the day with a text, 'His mercy endureth for ever' and 'The Lord is good'. The direct connection between the weather and what could be done on the farm is always there. Bright, warm, April-like weather in February 1909 leads to a flurry of sowing, harrowing and rolling. On the morning of 21 July 1910 rain beats on Will's window and a rough wind is blowing and the hay is untouched and almost spoilt. Under these conditions it was difficult to know how to be occupied and the carters were put on cart greasing and oiling harness. Will uses the words 'caddling' and 'shackling' for looking round for odd jobs. 3 September 1910 the weather is 'lovely' and corn carting goes on all day, with Will loading and pitching alternately and the ladies of the household bringing a picnic tea down to the farm so as not to hold up operations. Farming is not without its pleasures. On 30 October 1910, 'Oh dear the mud, never before did I get about in so much or get so splashed and dirty. My coat falls off the horse's hames into a ditch full of water and mud and is run over by the cart coming out all mud-begrimed and wet'. The farm was low-lying and subject to flooding, hence Will's never-ending job of treating the sheep's feet for foot-rot. Will says quite simply, 'I don't like farming when it's wet' and we can visualise his getting soaked driving in a pony trap or riding a bicycle and having nothing like the protective clothing available today, boots and gaiters rather than Wellingtons, a thick overcoat rather than oil skins.

Will's position in the Venn household was perhaps somewhat ambiguous, he refers to himself wryly as 'the lodger'. He had his own room and lived with the family, being made use of as chaperone and coachman by the girls returning from evening visits, going to and from the station and attending chapel on Sunday. He enjoyed flirting with the eldest daughter, Manna (Gift of God) and felt very happy the day before she was due back on holiday, but could do very little about it on 2s. 6d. a week. 24 September 1909 reads, 'Have a bit of a lark with the girls in the evening. Manna and I are locked out, but our merriment is short lived, for it upsets the Governor and makes him rather cross, so that we have to retire to bed rather solemnly'. All the hallmarks of a heavy Victorian father are there. Will of course, as far as the men were concerned, was on the side of the Boss and often had to deputise for him when he was away or feeling 'seedy'. He was not averse to obliging the ladies making a little duck trough or picking plums for jam making.

Dial Post today is in a pocket of countryside that has escaped change. The Burrell family have owned the land for generations and the farmers have remained tenants. In some ways there are less facilities than in Will's time, the Burrell Arms where rent and rate audits took place was demolished ten years ago to make way for a dual carriageway, and there is no village shop. There was until recently a farm pupil at Dial Post but, unlike Will, he ran a car, lived in his own house and was very well paid.

By September 1910, with the end of his apprenticeship in sight, Will and Father started looking at farms. They got a good impression of Hydehurst Farm Crawley, as did brother Sid. Mr. Venn pronounced favourably on the farm and in October he and Father met the agent and 'all is settled most satisfactorily, Praise the Lord'. On Thursday December 1 Will and Father drove over in the car (pony carriage) and agreed possession for 16 January 1911 .

The diary ends on 23 December 1910 with Will spending a very enjoyable evening with the girls, it being Kathleen's birthday. From now he would be putting into practice what he had learnt and recorded, until his call-up late in 1918 and untimely death from pneumonia after the Armistice.

PRELIMINARY NOTES

Terms of my apprenticeship with Mr. Venn as settled on Thursday February 4th 1909:

1. Apprenticeship to last two years from January 1st 1909, I having had one month on trial.
2. I am to receive 2/6 per week for the whole term of two years.
3. Premium £50 paid down by Father on February 4th 1909.
4. £1 per week to be paid for my board and lodging for the two years.
5. I am to be paid for every rabbit caught (nil).

Characters Mentioned in this Diary

Hunt	Head carter
George	Under carter till March 25th, afterwards labourer
Moore	Under carter, starting March 25th.
Lucas	Labourer
Banfield	Handy man
Steve	Carter's boy
Abbey	Labourer
Cheesmore	Labourer at Rooklands
Kempshall	Cowman

Names of Places Mentioned Herein

Lindfield	Set of buildings near house
Old Barn	Set of buildings about the middle of the farm
Honeypool	Set of buildings at extreme end of farm
New Barn	Farm buildings

Mangolds

Cost of crop per acre

Clearing ground after harvest   6/- per acre
Dung 30 load per acre   £3
Ploughing   10/-
Twice dragged   5/-
Twice rolled   2/6
Twice harrowed   2/-
Drilling   3/-
Harrowing after drill   1/-
Artificial manure 4 cwt. per acre   24/-
Seed   4/3
Hoeing   £1
Rent Rates Taxes   £1
Lifting and carting   3/-

    Total per acre   £8. 0. 9.

1909

A record of my life and work at Dial Post Farm, during the year 1909

God is faithful who hath promised

Friday January 1. I drive Mother into Horsham in the morning through the slush and we have our photos taken at Hobbs and mother buys various things to fit her boy out for leaving home. A never to be forgotten day.

Saturday January 2. Went to Mr. Venns to start learning the farming. Went over the farm in the afternoon. The first day of a new life, in a new home, feeling very strange.
 'The Lord is good'.

Sunday January 3. Went to Billingshurst in the morning. Saw Mother and Father after an absence of one night.

Monday January 4. Went carpentering with Mr. Venn, putting up a small shed. Grace went away. Still feeling very strange. Got on fairly well with the work.

Tuesday January 5. The threshing tackle arrived at the farm making a rare lot of mud and mess.

Wednesday January 6. Started threshing an oat rick. Had a hard day's work pitching bundles of straw.

Thursday January 7. Medicine for a cow suffering from Gargit or swollen quarters: Three quarter pounds salts, two ounces salt petre, mixed with a little treacle, making about one and a half pints and given in the form of a drench. The affected quarters to be fomented with warm water and well rubbed with camphorated oil once daily. Drench to be warm when given.

Monday January 11. Up at six o'clock, down to the farm with Mr. Venn, set the men to work. Went to Honeypool and fed the dry cows with wheat,

'Set the men to work hauling muck'

straw and roots. Back to the farm, cracked the sheep's cake and fed them and then home to breakfast. Made a manger for the heifers at Lindfield in the afternoon, then had a walk round the farm with Mr. Venn.

'His mercy endureth for ever'.

Tuesday January 12. Up at six o'clock, down to the farm with the boss. Went to Honeypool and served the dry cows with wheat and straw and roots. Caked the sheep and home to breakfast. Helped Mr. Venn fold the sheep after breakfast by carrying him the hurdles, making my shoulders rather sore. Walked over to Old Barn in the afternoon. Spent a very pleasant evening indoors.

Weather. Bright and fine.

Wednesday January 13. Went down to farm first thing with Mr. Venn and set the men to work straw hauling. After breakfast helped sack up some oats. Went to Steyning market in the afternoon, sold seven little pigs, 3 at 14s. and 4 at 17s. 6d., brought home a Dutch calf.

Weather. Drizzling rain and cold.

Friday January 15. Up at twenty past six. Went to Honeypool and fed the dry cows with roots and old hay, then home to breakfast. Drove Manna, Nellie and Kathleen into Horsham getting home about half past one. Went round with Mr. Venn and inspected the cows and young stock. Had a very easy day, or a day's mike.

Weather. Dirty but very fine overhead.

Saturday January 16. Men set to work at muck hauling. Did some carpentering after breakfast, putting up a hay rack. Pitched for the sheep in the afternoon. Mr. Venn sold a fat cow for £17.

Weather. Cold wind and very dirty.

Sunday January 17. Sunday, went to Billingshurst in the morning. Saw Mother and Father there. The meeting of loved ones is sweet.

Weather. Fine and bright.

Monday January 18. Set the men on ploughing up Clover Field. Fed the cows at Honeypool with straw and roots and then home to breakfast. Pitched for the sheep and sorted out sacks in the morning and made two troughs for the heifers at Old Barn in the afternoon.

Weather. Very windy but fine.

Tuesday January 19. Drove Manna to the station after breakfast, had a very pleasant ride although raining. Started cutting chaff at ten o'clock and did not finish until seven o'clock having cut two tons two cwt., the price charged by Mr. Venn being £3. 13*s*. 9*d*. per ton. A hard day's work with plenty of flour and dust. Felt Manna's going rather.

Weather. Damp and dull.

Wednesday January 20.   Up at the usual hour. Sent the carter off to the station with the chaff, the other men carting hurdles from the turnips on to the swedes. Went to Horsham in the morning with the boss, took Kathleen to the station, had a look round the market and then home. Pitched the first fold on the swedes for the sheep in the afternoon. A new plough arrived.

Weather. Cold and bright.

Thursday January 21.   Set the carters on ploughing up leigh.[1] Had a look round the farm in the morning, viewing the stock, etc. Went down to Lindfield in the afternoon and put up a hay rack for one cow and drove the sheep down to Thistly Field and started feeding them on cut swedes. Had a light day's work, feeling rather dull. The threshing tackle arrives again.

Weather. Cold and gloomy.

Friday January 22.   Up at six o'clock. Went down to the farm and set the men ploughing in the Clover Field. Fed the dry cows at Honeypool with mangolds and rough hay, served the sheep with cut swedes, cake and hay and then home to breakfast. Messrs. Norman, Selway and Paine came over and we had a day's rabbit shooting, killing about thirty-five rabbits and two hares. Had a fairly enjoyable day.

Weather. Cold wind, but dry.

Saturday January 23.   Went down to the farm and set the two carters and Jack ploughing in Upton's field. Served the dry cows and fed the sheep with cut swedes, cake (cotton and linseed) and hay, then home to breakfast. Went down to Thistly field and pitched a fold for the sheep and fed them again at midday. Fed them again at four o'clock with pulped swedes. The clover seeding tackle again breaks down, squashing the drum. Manna's message to me by Nellie was, 'Do all the good you can in whatever way you can'.

Weather. A bitter wind but nice and dry.

Monday January 25.   Set the two carters and Jack on ploughing. Fed the sheep with twelve bushels of cut swedes. After breakfast helped sack up forty sacks of oats, after which we caked the sheep and gave them six bushels of cut roots. In the afternoon the boss and I went rabbiting, getting nine. My ferret got lost, having to leave it all night.

A fine, bright, clear day.

---

1 Ley or Lea – arable land laid down for pasture or grassland.

Tuesday January 26.   Up at the usual hour and set three ploughs ploughing in Upton's field. Fed the cows at Honeypool and served the sheep with twelve baskets of cut swedes, and then home to breakfast. Walked about the farm in the morning and fed the sheep at midday. Went rabbiting with the boss after dinner killing only four. Galvanized bin arrives.

Weather. A fine bright clear day.

Wednesday January 27.   Downstairs at twenty past six. Set three ploughs ploughing in Upton's field which was finished today except for the headlands. Went rabbiting with Mr. Venn after breakfast killing two and finding the lost ferret but losing another. Killed another couple after dinner. A fine day's sport. A new turnip cutter arrives for the sheep.

Weather. Raw cold and misty, very unpleasant.

Thursday January 28.   Sent the carters to the station with forty-six sacks of oats, twenty-three each. Messrs. Salway and Hicks arrive after breakfast for a day's shooting, which we had, killing twenty-three rabbits. Came home and had a high tea, then went into the drawing room and had a chat, the principal topic of conversation being about heifers and slipcalf.

Weather. Very cold and misty first but fine later.

Friday January 29.   Performed the usual morning's duties feeding cows and sheep. Set the men to work hauling out dung onto the land. Went to Partridge Green in the morning with Mr. Venn to try and find out a rabbiter, which he did. I had my back mudguard repaired at a cost of 0s. 7d. Had an early dinner and went rabbiting in the afternoon with the boss. Had better luck this time killing thirteen.

Weather. Very cold first thing but much warmer afternoon.

Saturday January 30.   Went through the usual morning routine of feeding dry cows and sheep. Went round the farm after breakfast with Mr. Venn and inspected all the stock, taking us nearly all the morning. In the afternoon I prepared for going home with a happy heart. Started away about half past three and arriving about half past four, receiving a hearty welcome from my dear ones. May, Capel, Sid and Amy also arrive at Lucerne.

Weather. Cold wind but dry.

Sunday January 31.   I enjoy a Sunday at home. Sid and I make a tour of inspection. A very happy day.

Monday February 1.   Got up about eight. After breakfast Sid, Amy V. and I drive into Horsham with Topsy. Had two front shoes put on, spending about three quarters of an hour in the town. We drive home round

Warnham. Had an early dinner, clipping Topsy's mane off afterwards. Had a game of Bagatelle in the afternoon. About twenty past four I start off for Dial Post after spending a delightful weekend in communion with my loved ones. I feel the parting with loved ones terribly. I arrive at Dial Post just in time for tea. My heart is full of my week-end at home.

Weather. Warm, damp and cloudy.

Tuesday February 2. Sent the two carters and Jack ploughing in Eight Acres field. After breakfast I helped the boss pitch a fold for the sheep and served them with cut swedes. Did a little rabbiting after dinner, again losing the ferret. Two calves arrive, the one from a heifer dying and the one from the cow alright.

Weather. Dry and frosty in the morning, very dirty later but fine.

Wednesday February 3. Mr. Venn goes off to market and I am left on my own. I feed the sheep at dinner time and again at four o'clock, they having had all day fourteen baskets full and three trusses of hay amongst 110 sheep. Our new lodger Winnie Williams arrives.

Weather. Windy damp and dirty, but dry overhead.

Thursday February 4. Was ten minutes late this morning. Set the two carters and Jack ploughing. Jack and George in Lashmers field and Hunt in Upton's. Served the dry cows and sheep with their usual rations. Mother and Father arrive about two and things are settled up regarding my apprenticeship.

Weather. Windy, fine and bright, quite warm.

Friday February 5. Went down to the farm on our bikes and set the two carters and Jack ploughing. Shot four rabbits with Mr. Venn in the morning. In the afternoon the boss went to Ashington while I dug some carrots in the garden and walked over to Old Barn after some rabbits. Served the sheep again at tea time.

Weather. Very windy, but beautifully fine and dry.

Saturday February 6. The boss was late this morning so went down to the farm by myself and set the two carters and Jack ploughing in Thistly field. Killed six rabbits in the morning. Fed the sheep in the afternoon and evening. Gave the carters their corn and then home to tea feeling rather tired.

Weather. Very fine bright and dry.

Monday February 8. Mr. and Mrs. Venn drive over to Mr. Norman's for the day, leaving us on our own. I am left to look after the farm. I pitch a fold in the morning and serve the sheep at noon. After dinner I crack two lots of sheep cake and have a turn at ploughing with the carter's plough.

Weather. Cold but very bright and fine.

Tuesday February 9.   Set the carter and George ploughing in Thistly field. Fed the dry cows and served the sheep. It came on to rain after dinner time so we had to pitch a dry fold in the afternoon, a very wet dirty job. Came home to tea feeling very grubby and hungry.
Weather. Cold in the morning, but very wet and dirty in the afternoon.

Wednesday February 10.   Up at six. Went down to the farm with Mr. Venn and set the carter and George ploughing in Clapperfield. The boss went to Steyning market about half past eleven leaving me on my own. In the afternoon I loaded my first load of straw, after which I carried some hurdles for a fold and fed the sheep at tea time. I then came back to the farm and gave the carters their corn and went round and saw that the seeding tackle and seed were alright and then home to tea after a fairly hard day.
Weather. Fine but damp till five o'clock when it came on to rain.

Thursday February 11.   Went down to the farm with Mr. Venn and set the men on carting muck from the rick yard. Fed the sheep and moved them onto a hard fold and then home to breakfast. In the afternoon we went and shot four rabbits, dressed some of the sheep's feet for foot rot with Learners Cure, served them again and then home to tea.
Weather. Very wet first thing, clearing up later.

Friday February 12.   Up at six. Set the two carters ploughing in Clapper field. In the morning Mr. Venn shows his brother round the farm, while I put a new tyre on the front wheel of my bike. I went ploughing in the afternoon for some time with Hunt's help, got on very well for a start. Abbey and I fed the sheep at four o'clock Mr. Venn not feeling very well.
Weather. A very bitter wind but nice and dry.

Saturday February 13.   Carters and Jack ploughing in Clapper field. Fed the cows at Honeypool and served the sheep. I pitched a fold in the afternoon. Clapper field is finished all except the headlands.
Weather. Cold and bright.

Sunday February 14.   Went to Billingshurst in the morning with Mr. Venn. Saw Mother and Father and received several goodies and remedies for chaps from home and a loving Mother.

Monday February 15.   Up at the usual hour. Went down to the farm with the boss and set the two carters ploughing the headland in Clapper field and Jack in Gurze field into which the carters went after finishing Clapper. I started pitching a fold after breakfast but was called away to help the governor rabbit. Fed the sheep with Lucas' help tea time. Caught six rabbits during the day.

Weather. A beautiful bright mild day.

Tuesday February 16.   Up at six. Went down to the farm with Mr. Venn, and set the two carters and Jack ploughing Gurze field. Fed the cows at Honeypool myself and the sheep with Abbey's help. Helped Mr. Venn sack up twenty sacks of oats in the afternoon and got the winnowing machine ready for the clover seed. The sheep got out after tea so I had to go down and get them in, having rather a dark walk.

Weather. Very bright and warm.

Wednesday February 17.   Sent the carter to West Grinstead with ten quarters of oats bringing back two ton of cotton cake. In the afternoon we drilled about four acres of black oats. Served the sheep myself at tea time. Mr. Stanton came causing much talking in the evening.

Weather. Very fine and warm.

Thursday February 18.   Went down to the farm and set the two carters, Jack, Lucas and Abbey sowing and harrowing in oats in Pond field which was finished. Carried some hurdles for a fold in the morning which we pitched in the afternoon. Killed five rabbits. One and three quarter ton mangolds are carted away by Mr. Gouch out of eleven tons bought by the boss.

Weather. Very bright and warm.

Friday February 19.   Five minutes late this morning. Set the men on dung cart. Went to Partridge Green after the Vet for a sick cow. In the afternoon Mr. Venn goes to Pulborough and buys six heifers at £19. 10s. 0d. apiece. I have the oversight of the sheep during his absence.

Weather. Very bright and warm (April-like).

Saturday February 20.   Again five minutes late. Fed the cows at Honeypool, served the sheep and cracked some cake. In the afternoon the men went drilling white oats in Uptons, pulling in and finishing off about five acres. Mr. Stanton arrives again for the week-end.

Weather. Very bright and warm.

Monday February 22.   Went down to the farm with the gov. and set the men on dung cart for the morning. Went swede trimming in the morning (a fresh experience for me). In the afternoon the men went oat drilling in Uptons field, the ground working beautifully. The boss and I pitched a fold for the sheep and served them at tea time.

Weather. Bright and healthy.

Tuesday February 23. After breakfast I cycled to Dean Hill Crossway to meet some heifers which Kempshall and I drove home. Mr. Venn went to Worthing with some rabbits to Mr. Whittington obtaining 10s. 6d. per dozen. In the afternoon the men drilled two and a quarter sacks of white oats in Uptons and then went dung cart again, it being too frosty to continue.

Weather. Not quite so bright as yesterday and colder.

Wednesday February 24. After breakfast Mr. Venn goes to Horsham and Steyning markets, again leaving me on my own. Gave the heifers twelve basketfuls of roots at noon, having fetched the cutter and troughs etc. from Old Barn. Served the sheep myself at dinner and tea times. In the afternoon the two carters went ploughing in Thistly field. I pitched a fold for the sheep and fed the heifers again with hay.

Weather. Bright, clear and fine.

Thursday February 25. We had a look round at the stock, etc. in the morning. In the afternoon we pitched a fold for the sheep and did a few odd jobs. The governor goes to Ashington with forty rabbits in the evening.

Weather. Very cold and dull.

Friday February 26. Up at the usual time and set the men on dung cart all day. Have a bit of a mooch about in the morning, the governor being busy with Trim in cow dealing. Pitched a fold and fed the sheep and heifers. The boss sells six cows to Trim.

Weather. Very cold wind, dull and a little snowy.

Saturday February 27. Set the men carting rubble into the manure yard for filling it up. Mr. Venn and his brother go to Leatherhead for the day to look at a farm. In the afternoon I tried to mend a puncture for Mr. Venn, having a pretty good job. Fed the sheep and heifers in the afternoon.

Weather. Cold, bleak and dismal.

Sunday February 28. I cycled home and spent a few very pleasant hours, returning at half past six.

Monday March 1. Went down to the farm with the boss and set the men clearing away the muck from the mangold pie. In the afternoon the carters went ploughing in Thistly field and Jack mangold hauling. Did a little ploughing in the afternoon. Started giving the sheep cake in the evening, giving one and a half cotton and two and a half linseed in the evenings.

Weather. A dull day and cold, rather inclined to snow.

Tuesday March 2. Downstairs at six twenty, and sent Hunt after some seed oats and George, Lucas and Jack hauling rubble and harrowing in Uptons in the afternoon. I rode into Horsham in the morning with the engine lamp getting back about one o'clock. The mangold pie in the rick yard is started. I am not feeling at all well today, having a very heavy cold and not at all work sharp.

Weather. Cold, but brighter than yesterday.

Wednesday March 3.   Up at the usual time and set the men on carting dirt into the yard. Fed the heifers at Honeypool and the sheep and then home to breakfast. The shafts of the milk cart are broken owing to the horse going down caused by the slipperyness of the roads there having been rather a heavy fall of snow during the previous night. I serve the sheep at dinner and tea time, Mr. Venn going to Steyning market. Carried some hurdles for a fold in the afternoon, otherwise there is very little doing the ground being covered with snow. Sussex bull sold at Steyning market for £12. 10s. 0d.

Weather. Cold and dreary, snow falling in the afternoon, very unpleasant.

Thursday March 4.   Had a look round the stock in the morning. Did some rook starving[1] in the afternoon. A very unpleasant day getting about in the snow and slush.

Weather. A little warmer, much snow about.

Friday March 5.   Set the men hauling rubble into the yard and outside the stable. Pitched a fold and served the sheep myself in the afternoon. Mrs. Venn goes away, being summoned by a telegram to Wellington, Kathleen being ill.

Weather. Bitterly cold before breakfast, brightening up and getting much warmer later, snow still about.

Saturday March 6.   Mr. Venn buys a four gallon cow (Primrose) for £18. 15s. 0d.

Up at six-twenty and set the men winnowing oats in the morning. Fed heifers and sheep and then home to breakfast. Did not do much in the morning. Started unpacking Mr. Venn's incubator, after being packed for over a year. In the afternoon the men went sacking up oats in the granary. We shifted the sheep into the dry fold, it being very wet and dirty. I was right glad to get home, the boss and I being wet through. My worst experience of farming as yet.

Weather. A pouring wet day, the snow disappears.

Sunday March 7.   Prevented from going to Billingshurst by floods.

---

1   Shooting.

Monday March 8. Went down to the farm and set George ploughing in Short Lanes field, the carter taking some oats to Mr. Tidey in the morning and bringing back a load of coal, he going to plough in the afternoon in Short Lanes. In the morning Mr. Venn goes to see a Dutch cow. I litter up the Honeypool hovels and serve the sheep at dinner time. We have a look round the stock, etc., in the afternoon.

Weather. Fine and warm.

Tuesday March 9. Set the two carters ploughing in Short Lanes field and Lucas repairing a drain across the road. In the afternoon I clean up Mr. Venn's incubator and do a little ploughing. A telegram is received from Wellington to say that the crisis of Kathleen's illness has passed favourably.

Weather. Dull and mild.

Wednesday March 10. Up at six. Went down to the farm by myself, Mr. Venn going off soon after seven to Chichester market. So I have the management of the farm during the whole day. I serve the sheep and heifers and then come home to breakfast, after which I help load a fat sow, then I go down to the sheep and feed them giving Abbey orders about shifting the troughs, etc. After dinner I pack up three dozen rabbits for Worthing going over to Burgess' for a box and having a long chat with him. Fed the sheep at tea time, coming home to finish packing the rabbits, and then back to the farm again. The carters go ploughing in Shorts Lanes field today. The lodgers have a day on their own. I have an accident and break one of the hammers on the gun.

Weather. Dull and humid.

Thursday March 11. Set the carters ploughing and George fetching a load of litter for the sheep. After breakfast Abbey and I shifted the sheep troughs, etc. back to the hard fold, a very dirty job. In the afternoon Hunt ploughs in Carter's field, George and Abbey litter up Honeypool yard. I finish up by serving the sheep and heifers.

Weather. Dull, dirty and unpleasant.

Friday March 12. Up at six o'clock set Hunt ploughing in Carter's field, George taking some litter to litter up Lindfield yard. In the morning I mend a puncture in Mr. Venn's front tyre. He and I feeding the sheep at dinner time. Lucas hedging all day.

Weather. Dull, cold and unpleasant.

Saturday March 13. Set the men carting out rubbish from around the oat rick at Old Barn into the meadow. After breakfast the boss and I burn up a lot of thorns in Thistly field and serve the sheep at dinner time. In the

'Set the two carters ploughing'

Horse hoeing

afternoon I prepare with a happy heart for the week end at Lucerne arriving there about four twenty.

Weather. Cold wind, unsettled.

Monday March 15. I spend a night amongst the feathers[1] at Lucerne getting down to breakfast about eight. Have a look round in the morning and do a few jobs in the bee house. Start for Dial Post again soon after eleven, Father driving me as far as Tenchford, and I get here about half past twelve. In the morning the men go carting muck into Oxons meadow. The boss and I attend to the sheep's foot rot.

Weather. Dull in the morning, snowing all the afternoon.

Tuesday March 16. In the morning the boss and I dress a lot of the sheep for foot rot, feeding them at dinner time. In the afternoon we winnow out three bushels of clover seed and drive the sheep through a foot bath. Lucas hedging most of the day. Blackbird's calf arrives.

Weather. Cold but a little brighter.

Wednesday March 17. Set the men on muck cart into Oxons meadow. The boss goes to Horsham and Steyning markets for the day. I carry across one lot of cake to the sheep and the hurdles and start pitching a fold. In the afternoon the two carters plough where the mangold pie stood in Uptons. Jack going slush cart. Have a long chat with Burgess after dinner. I finish up by serving the sheep and heifers with Abbey's help and giving the carters their oats. Lucas hedging all day.

Weather. Cold but bright, getting much warmer towards evening.

Thursday March 18. After breakfast I have a little chat with Burgess and then I have to go to Shipley after some meat for dinner. The carter fetches two ton of linseed cake in the morning. In the afternoon we winnow ten sacks of clover seed. Mr. Venn brings home a calf. I miss my home rather.

Weather. Warm, dull and very wet afternoon.

Friday March 19. Set the men carting muck into Oxons meadow, Hunt going to the station after two ton of cotton cake. After breakfast Mr. Venn shows his brother round the farm. I help unload the cake and feed the sheep at dinner time. The heap of muck is finished.

Weather. Mild and unsettled.

Saturday March 20. After breakfast I clean up my bike and straighten the back wheel, after which I go down to the farm and mooch about until it is time to feed the sheep. After dinner the boss and I have a walk round. A

---

1 i.e. in a feather bed.

very slack day. The governor goes butter making in the morning, teaching Winnie.

Weather. Mild and unsettled.

Monday March 22.   Up at six o'clock and set all hands clearing out muck from the rick yard into Oxons meadow all day. In the morning Mr. Venn drives to Steyning after some vitriol while I have a walk round and feed the sheep at dinner time. The two lodgers dine together today. After dinner I mend a slight burst in my tyre and make a foot bath for the sheep.

Weather. Damp and very dirty underfoot.

Tuesday March 23.   After breakfast we litter up the Honeypool hovels and feed the sheep. In the afternoon the boss stays in to do some writing while I finish littering up and feed sheep and heifers.

Weather. A very humid atmosphere, still very dirty.

Wednesday March 24.   Went down to the farm with the boss and set the men carting out muck at Honeypool. Hunt going to fetch the new carter's furniture. After breakfast I have a chat with Burgess, then going down to the farm and cracked some sheep's cake, stopped up some mouse holes under the granary and served the sheep myself at dinner time. We have a good long dinner hour and then go down to the farm and do a little to clover seed, finishing up by serving the sheep. Was glad to get indoors by the fire.

Weather. A wet day, very dirty and messy.

Thursday March 25.   Up at the usual hour. Went down to the farm and set the men on muck cart, Lucas hedging. The new carter and his boy start to-day. In the morning we have a walk round viewing the wheat plant, etc., and drive the sheep from Thistly field to Honeypool meadow. After dinner I see to the shifting of the sheep's troughs, etc., and trim some mangolds at Honeypool.

Weather. Showery with bright intervals.

Friday March 26.   In the morning I do a bit of trap washing, mend a puncture, have a look round at the men, do some mangold trimming, give the sheep some hay and then home to dinner. In the afternoon I cart a load of mangolds to the sheep and feed the heifers at tea time. The boss goes to a sale at Theale, Slinfold, making Lucerne a half-way house. I have a letter from Amy V. Sid being unwell.

Weather. Dry overhead, cloudy with sunny intervals.

Saturday March 27.   In the morning the boss and I go over to Mr. Wing's after two weaners bought at the sale at Theale, Slinfold. In the afternoon I

trim some mangolds, get a cart-load and take up to the sheep and also some hay. Mr. Venn cut his finger in a root pulper and rendered almost helpless.
  Weather. Much brighter and better.

Monday March 29. Downstairs at six twenty. Went down to the farm with the boss and set the carters muck cart from the rick yard. Lucas, George and Abbey dung spreading. In the morning Banfield and I fetch some hurdles from Thistly field and trough for making foot bath. In the afternoon I litter the Honeypool hovels and take a load of mangolds to the sheep and feed them and then have a look round at the dung spreaders. Mr. Venn feeling queer so stayed in all the afternoon.
  Weather. Fine morning, showery afternoon.

Tuesday March 30. Went down to the farm by myself the boss feeling unwell. Set the carters and Jack dung cart, Lucas and Abbey spreading in Oxons. Fed the heifers and sheep before breakfast. After breakfast I do some writing for Mr. Venn, then go down to the farm, have a look round and trim some mangolds at Honeypool. In the afternoon I crack some cake for the sheep, cart some mangolds up to them and feed them and the heifers.
  Mud mud everywhere today.
  Weather. Almost another wet day.

Wednesday March 31. In the morning we have a walk round the farm and drive the sheep through a foot bath. In the afternoon I go with the milk cart and Kitty to the mill after some meal getting back to the farm about four o'clock. Fed sheep and heifers and finished up by giving the carters their oats.
  Weather. A drizzly rain nearly all day.
  A very wet, unkindly month, could not sow an oat.

Thursday April 1. Went down to the farm by myself the boss being unwell and set Hunt and Jack bedding up Lindfield and Honeypool yards, afterwards going muck cart with Moore Lucas and George, spreading in Oxons meadow. I feed heifers and sheep before breakfast. In the morning I knock about lumps of dirt after Abbey has spread it. In the afternoon I turn over heaps of hedge trimmings in Crab Tree field in order to preserve the clover underneath and take some mangolds up to the sheep. Mr. Venn gets out after breakfast.
  Weather. April opens dull with a little rain, rather colder.

Friday April 2. Set Moore and Jack picking up hedge trimmings, after which Moore starts rolling the seeds in Crab Tree field. Hunt goes to the station after one ton of meal and one ton of cotton cake. He and Jack go hurdle cart after dinner. In the morning I cart a load of mangolds up to the sheep. The rest of the day till four o'clock George and I trim and dress their feet. Mr. Venn goes to the horse sale at Steyning.

Weather. Frost in the morning but a much brighter day.

Saturday April 3.   Went down to the farm by myself, the boss again being queer. Set Hunt chain harrowing in Oxons and Moore finishing rolling in Crab Tree field and then going bush harrowing in the seeds next to Hovel field. Lucas spreading at Honeypool. In the afternoon George and I start doing the sheep's feet again. Mr. Venn drives to the station to fetch Mrs. Venn and Kathleen.

Weather. Very bright and warm.

Sunday April 4.   Went to Billingshurst in the morning with Mr. Venn, saw Mother, Father and Sid.

Monday April 5.   Up at six and set the men sowing black oats in Eight Acres. In the morning Mr. Venn and I have a stroll round to find out the condition of the ground. In the afternoon we winnow some clover seed. I drive to the station with six bushels for Mr. Passmore of Applesham Farm. Have a chat with Burgess in the evening.

Weather. Very bright and genial.

Tuesday April 6.   Set the men sowing black oats in Lashmers field which is finished by dinner time. In the morning we sack up some clover seed. In the afternoon the men go sowing white oats in Uptons finishing it off while we finish winnowing the clover seed and get it all sacked up ready for travelling. In the evening Mr. Venn and I have a ride to Partridge Green to see some heifers.

Weather. Frost in the morning but very bright.

Wednesday April 7.   Up at the usual hour. Set the men sowing white oats in Thistly field. In the morning I put the sheep through a foot bath and finish sacking up the clover seed forty-four bushels of which I send off in the afternoon. The boss stays in in the afternoon feeling unwell so I have the farm to myself. I help Lucas sack up some patent manure and have a stroll round to see them sowing and then to have a look at the oats that were put in in February, and are coming up strong and thick. Finished up by serving the sheep and heifers.

Weather. Frost first thing very bright and hot later.

Thursday April 8.   Set the men on sowing oats in Rushets field. In the morning the boss and I have a look round and litter up the weaners at Lindfield. In the afternoon Mr. Venn goes to Church Farm sale taking

Nellie and me. I drive from there with Nellie to the station to meet Manna. I prepare to go home starting about half past five, going round Horsham arriving home about half past seven.

Weather. Very bright and very warm.

Friday April 9. Lay in bed till nearly half past eight with my old mate Sid. We have a look round the premises after breakfast and then May, Sid, Amy and I have a walk round Itchingfield Church. In the afternoon Sid and I have a drive round Warnham through Horsham and have a game of tennis. In the evening we have another game of tennis, have a game of patience and after supper retire to bed.

Weather. Very bright.

Saturday April 10. Downstairs to eight o'clock breakfast. Sid drives May to Horsham while I stay at home expecting Mr. Freeman who comes about eleven and we look through the bees together, taking some time to do so. In the evening Amy and I walk to the station with Sid who returns to Worthing after nearly a fortnight's sick leave.

Weather. Glorious.

Sunday April 11. Mother, Father and Amy go to Billingshurst while I stay home and mind house. In the afternoon an old debtor of Father's arrives (Mr. Macklewane).

Monday April 12. Bank Holiday. Once again eight o'clock breakfast. After breakfast I start cleaning up the bee house and also shallow frames ready for the season's use. Father and I drive into Horsham with Girlie and from there to Slinfold station to collect some paint. I finish the bee house when I get back. After dinner I see to the mowing machine and do some odd jobs. Have an early tea and again start for Dial Post reaching it about a quarter past seven after a most happy time at home.

Weather. Fairly bright morning, inclined to rain afternoon.

Tuesday April 13. Went down to the farm and set the men on, Hunt going to the station after some mangold manure, Moore harrowing wheat, George rolling in Tenchford field. Finished oat sowing today. In the afternoon I take a load of mangolds and straw to Dial Post.

Weather. Dull and inclined to rain.

Wednesday April 14. Set Hunt first rolling the wheat, then going into Lashmers field rolling after seed. Moore harrowing in Lashmers before Lucas who is sowing clover seed. George harrowing first in the wheat field, then in Tenchford. After breakfast Mr. Venn drives into Horsham with Grace and Manna. I get some oats sacked up ready to take to the mill where

I go in the afternoon. Did the usual feeding of sheep and heifers during the day.

Weather. Dull morning, brighter afternoon.

Thursday April 15. Up at the usual time. Went down to the farm with the boss and set Hunt rolling wheat, George rolling in Lashmers and Moore harrowing in same. In the afternoon George harrows in ten acres, Moore rolls in Tenchford. I take mangolds, hay and cake to the sheep before breakfast. In the morning Mr. Venn and I dress the sheep's feet. In the afternoon we all go to Floodgates in honour of Mrs. Venn's birthday. Mr. Venn and I soon leave and cycle to West Grinstead to Mr. Tidey's.

Weather. Bright and warm.

Friday April 16. Set Hunt cultivating in Hovel field. Moore rolling for the last time in Tenchford, George slush cart, drawing bushes and getting a load of straw from Old Barn for the cows. Did the usual work before breakfast of mangold cart, etc. In the morning we stay in and do a little settlement of various accounts. In the afternoon I help George load oat straw. Did the usual work of feeding the sheep and heifers. Mr. Venn gets very cross with Grace at tea time.

Weather. Fairly bright and warm.

Saturday April 17. Set Hunt cultivating in Hovel field and then Clapper field, Moore rolling in Pond field, George hay tying in the morning and rolling after Hunt in the afternoon. In the morning I take a load of hay to Lindfield and Dial Post. In the afternoon we have a walk round and attend to some of the sheep's feet. Do the usual day's work on the heifer and sheep feeding. Louise the skivvy departs.

Weather. Bright and warm.

Monday April 19. Up at six o'clock and set Hunt cultivating in Clapper field. Moore rolling oats first in Pond field and then in Uptons. George rolling in Clapper field after Hunt. In the afternoon I go to Shipley mill for meal. Do the usual day's feeding of stock. Another new maid arrives, number four since I have been at Dial Post.

Weather. Foggy first thing, very warm later, rain in the evening.

Tuesday April 20. Went down to the farm with the governor and set Hunt harrowing beans in Old Woods. Moore rolling first in Honeypool meadow and then in Crab Tree Croft. George chain harrowing in the morning in Crab Tree Croft and afternoon in Oxons meadow. Mr. Venn goes off to Guildford market early in the morning. I have a look round at the men in the morning. In the afternoon I take a barrel of water up to Honeypool and fetch some straw from Old Barn to Lindfield.

Weather. Very fresh and lovely after a good shower the previous evening.

Wednesday April 21.   Up at the usual time. Set Hunt cultivating and drilling tares in Gurze. Moore rolling tares in Gurze in the morning. In the afternoon Hunt harrows in the tares seed. In the morning I acted carter's boy in leading front horse of the drill. In the afternoon the governor and I go to Steyning market and buy two calves there which I go after in the evening to Mr. Pierce at Abbots Farm, Ashington, getting back about eight o'clock.

Weather. Cold first thing, much warmer later.

Thursday April 22.   Up at the usual time and set the men at work in Clapper field. Hunt and George harrowing and Moore rolling. After ten o'clock we start drilling the mangolds, Hunt's horse in the drill and George following. I take George's horses and harrows and harrow behind the drill, keeping on for the rest of the day. We finish sowing the field by doing an hour's overtime it coming on to rain hard just as we had finished. Did the usual feeding of stock. Feeling rather tired.

Weather. Bright first part raining later.

Friday April 23.   Rose as usual and set the men to work. Hunt rolling in Ten Acres. Moore harrowing in Ten Acres and Burchells in the morning, George rolling seed in Hovel field. After breakfast the boss and I have another go at the sheep's feet. In the afternoon Moore chain harrows Oxons meadow. I go to the mill and fetch home the pigs' meal. Have a letter from Mother to say that the cow (Primrose) is bad after calving.

Weather. Bright morning, damp afternoon.

Saturday April 24.   Awoke late this morning so had a mighty rush to get downstairs by six twenty. Set Hunt going to station for two ton of linseed cake, Moore chain harrowing in Burchells and Torey mead. George rolling in Oxons. In afternoon Hunt goes rolling in Oxons with Cambridge. In the afternoon I get a barrel of water for Honeypool, a load of straw from Old Barn for Dial Post and half a load of mangolds for sheep.

Weather. Fine and warm.

Sunday April 25.   To Billingshurst in the morning, driving Manna, Grace and Winnie. Dear old Primrose dies with milk fever.

Monday April 26.   Up at six twenty and set Hunt harrowing in Hovel field with the Larkworthy harrow. Moore rolling seed in Lashmers and then rolling the last sown oats in Uptons. George rolling wheat and doing odd jobs. The cows are turned out for the first time during the daytime. In the morning the boss and I have another go at the sheep's feet. In the afternoon I drive Mrs. Venn, Grace and Winnie into Horsham.

Weather. Very bright day, raining a little towards evening.

Tuesday April 27.   Went down to the farm with the boss and set Hunt rolling but was prevented about nine o'clock by rain so he and Banfield take a waggon load of cord wood to Dial Post. Moore working ground for cabbage and maize in Old Woods with lift harrow. In the morning I pitch the first fold for the sheep on rye and we shift them to it. Have a letter from Father in the morning telling me about the cow.

Weather. Showery and warm.

Wednesday April 28.   Set all hands at work in Hovel field, part dung cart and part spreading. Do the usual day's stock feeding and a bit of dung spreading in Hovel field.

Weather. Fine.

Thursday April 29.   Up at the usual time and set all hands at work in Hovel field, the two carters ploughing, the others dung cart and spreading. In the afternoon the governor and I have a walk over to Old Barn to have a look at the yearlings, etc., which have just been turned out to grass.

Weather. Fine morning, wet towards evening.

Friday April 30.   Went down to the farm and set the two carters ploughing in Hovel field, the rest of the men dung spreading. Lucas hoeing beans in Carter's field. Before breakfast I cake the sheep and give the stock at Old Barn a little hay and turn them out to grass. After breakfast Mr. Venn and I do a little to the sheep's feet once again. Today is Manna's birthday – the twenty first – so we have a high tea. I receive a present from Manna of a box of chocolates.

Weather. Stormy, bright intervals.

Saturday May 1.   Awoke late and had a rush to get down in time. Sent the carter to the station after some mangold manure. Moore ploughing in Hovel field, George harrowing in same. Lucas and Abbey hoeing beans. Hunt rolling with clod breaker after dinner, George with the Cambridge. In the morning Mr. Venn and I have a good go at the sheep's feet. In the afternoon I pitch two fold for the sheep, making my arms ache rather. Had a very busy day with the sheep, feeling rather tired.

Weather. Cold with snow showers.

Monday May 3.   Set Hunt harrowing (twice) Moore rolling with the Cambridge, and his boy rolling with the cylinder rollers. George went slush cart in the afternoon. I see to the sheep and turn out stock at Old Barn

before breakfast. In the morning I pitch and carry hurdles for a fold. Mr. Venn drives to Horsham to fetch a calf. Manna and Grace go away leaving us each a present of chocolate. I do seem to miss Manna somehow. Have a slack afternoon. Cows turned out by night.
Weather. Frost, fine and bright.

Tuesday May 4. Went down to the farm with the boss and set Hunt cultivating with heavy drags in Hovel field, Moore following him with the Cambridge roller. After ten o'clock Hunt starts drilling mangolds, Moore and Boy follow drill with wooden harrows and roller. We put in about five acres in Hovel field. In the afternoon I lead the front horse of the drill, making my legs ache. I purchase a tin of condensed milk for a snack.
Weather. A very fine day. A good shower would do good.

Wednesday May 5. Set the two carters ploughing in upper part of Hovel field, George and Lucas weeding in Pond field. I see to caking the sheep and feeding before breakfast. In the morning I am carrying hurdles and started pitching a fold. In the afternoon I finish pitching, crack some cake and send Abbey to Dial Post with some hay.
Weather. Frost, hot and very windy.

Thursday May 6. Up at the usual time and set the two carters ploughing in Hovel field. Stephen rolling oats in Eight acres, and rolling with clod crusher in Hovel field after finishing the oats. Lucas and George weeding in Pond field. In the afternoon I get twelve stakes ready for use and have a walk around to have a look at the work and look round to see that the young stock are alright. Mr. Venn goes off to Shoreham for the day.
Weather. Windy, hot, very tiring getting about.

Friday May 7. Sent Hunt to the station for two ton of manure (salt). Moore and George ploughing in Hovel field. After breakfast help Hunt unload the manure. I pitch the last fold on rye in Carters' field and we carry some hurdles to the rye in Old Woods field. A fairly slack day, have a bike ride with the gov. in the evening.
Weather. Very bright, windy, hot.

Saturday May 8. Up at the usual time. Sent Moore to the station after two tons of mangold manure. George and Hunt working the ground in Hovel field, Hunt harrowing, George rolling. We turn the sheep out to pasture again in the morning and have another go at their feet. I have a slack afternoon and cycle home in the evening.
Weather. Cold wind and bright.

Sunday May 9.   Cycle back to Dial Post in the evening in forty minutes after a very happy time.

Monday May 10.   Set all hands dung cart and spreading Hovel field (lower part of mangold ground). I walk round and see that the sheep are alright and drive between with the dung carts before breakfast. In the morning I make a frame to take the milk pans to go over the furnace, and take a barrel of water to Old Woods field for the sheep.
   Weather. Bright morning, hazy afternoon, very hot.

Tuesday May 11.   Up at the usual time, and set the two carters ploughing in Hovel field, the others dung spreading, except the boy who goes rolling with Cambridge roller directly after the ploughs. In the morning I go ploughing with Hunt's plough and do quite a lot. In the afternoon I get a fold ready for the sheep into which we drive them for the night. On the whole I have a very slack day. Daisy, the cart mare is taken ill with farcey.[1]
   Weather. Bright and sultry.

Wednesday May 12.   Went down to the farm with the boss and set Hunt and Moore ploughing in Hovel field. George and Lucas couching and dung spreading. In the afternoon we drill another piece (about three acres) to mangolds, Moore harrowing, Steve rolling behind the drill. In the morning I go rolling, in the afternoon I lead the front horse of the drill, and pitch a fold for the sheep and get them in. Have about an hour in my room in the evening sewing on buttons and mending, etc. Have a lot of walking today and feel rather tired.
   Weather. Bright and sultry – rain greatly needed.

Thursday May 13.   Up at the usual time. I see the sheep before breakfast. In the morning and part of the afternoon Banfield and I go hurdle cart from Carters field to Old Woods and I pitch a fold. The boss gets Old Barn ready for sheep shearers. I cycle over to Partridge Green to visit Mrs. Terry who is staying there, but cannot see her she being ill in bed.
   Weather. Not quite so bright, colder, dry.

Friday May 14.   I am by God's grace safely brought through another year.[2]
   Up at the usual hour. Went over to Mr. Atwater's to try and stop his coming to shear the sheep they having got wet overnight. Set the two carters ploughing in Hovel field, George, Lucas and Steve spreading dung. The boy goes harrowing meadows in the afternoon. Banfield and I go knocking about mole heaps in the morning. In the afternoon we get ready

1   Over-eating; to farce is to cram with food.
2   It is his eighteenth birthday.

soak, have a walk round and pen half the sheep in Old Barn hovel, getting home about fifteen minutes past eight. Very fresh and nice after a good rain the previous night.

Weather. Dull.

Saturday May 15. The sheep shearers come today so Banfield and I have to wait on them and have a hard day's work catching the sheep and tying up the fleeces. In the afternoon the last piece of Hovel field is drilled with mangolds, this finishing the field off.

Weather. Bright morning, dull afterwards and cold.

Monday May 17. Hunt cultivating and rolling for cabbage and maize in Old Woods, Moore and George ploughing for mangolds in Gurze field. After breakfast I cycle over to Mr. Bailey's, Eatons farm to see about some cabbage plants and pitch a fold for the sheep. In the afternoon we put the sheep into the rye and in the evening the boss and I drive over to fetch some of the cabbage plants (four thousand).

Weather. Fresh after rain the previous evening.

Tuesday May 18. George ploughing for cabbage in Old Woods, Abbey and Lucas planting cabbage plants after the plough. In the morning Steve goes to Eatons farm for eleven thousand cabbage plants. I am sorting and placing plants for the planters all day except part of the afternoon when I pitch a fold for the sheep.

Weather. Stormy with bright intervals.

Wednesday May 19. The two carters and Steve working down mangold ground in Gurze field. Hunt with heavy drags, the others with rollers. In the afternoon all hands at work in the Gurze couching.[1] The Governor not in a very good temper today.

Weather. Very bright and very hot.

Thursday May 20. A little late this morning my clock having stopped. Set all hands except Abbey and Lucas who were couching, dung cart from Lindfield yard to the Gurze. In the morning and part of the afternoon I drive between, later in the afternoon I pitch a fold for the sheep. Mother and Father come over to tea today and in the evening about half past six Sid and Bert cycle over from Worthing and Mr. Venn and I are measured for new suits. Mother and Father go home about seven and Sid and Bert about half past eight — have a very pleasant evening together.

Weather. Very bright and very hot again.

---

1 Removing couch grass.

Friday May 21. Up later this morning than I have been during my apprenticeship, getting down at ten to seven so have to sally forth alone. Set the two carters ploughing in dung in the Gurze. The other hands couching and spreading. Steve rolling behind plough. The governor is away all day at the rent and audit at the Burrell Arms.

Weather. Very bright and hotter than ever.

Saturday May 22. Managed to get up at the proper time this morning. The two carters harrowing and rolling piece for mangolds in the Gurze and afterwards drilling it with mangolds following same with harrow and roller. In the afternoon they go ploughing in the remaining piece of the Gurze. In the afternoon I prepare a fold for Sunday. I cycle to the top of the Bostel in the evening and meet Walter there, we have about an hour together.

Weather. Very bright and still hot.

Monday May 24. Set the men dung cart from Lindfield yard to the Gurze, and spreading. After breakfast the governor and I drive between with dung carts and finish pitching fold for sheep. Later I clean out the drill and sweep up the granary and see to the sheep.

Weather. Hot.

Tuesday May 25. Did not go down to the farm this morning, Banfield not being very well so had to stay and milk three cows. In the morning the boss and I have a walk over the farm viewing the crops, after a good rain the previous night. Hunt goes to the timber yard after sleepers, rails and posts for ditches. In the afternoon he goes salt sowing in Nine Corners. George and Lucas spar making. I drive Mrs. Venn, Nellie and Kathleen into Horsham.

Weather. Rather wet morning, fine afternoon.

Wednesday May 26. Set the two carters ploughing fallow in the Gurze. George and Lucas start mangold hoeing (rate £1 per acre) but are prevented from proceeding by rain. Steve chain harrowing at Honeypool, Nine Corners, etc. Lucas making drinking places for cattle. In the morning I do a good bit of ploughing with Hunt's plough. In the afternoon I pitch a fold and get the sheep from Crab Tree Croft.

Weather. Very windy with heavy storms.

Thursday May 27. Up at the usual time, set the two carters ploughing in the Gurze (fallow). After dinner Hunt goes ploughing in Short Lanes while Moore finishes headlands in Gurze. Lucas and George go hoeing mangolds in the afternoon in Clapper field. In the morning I do a little ploughing and set a fold. In the afternoon I go pulling out Charlock in the mangold drills and measure out ground with the governor for the hoers.

Weather. Cloudy and stormy.

Friday May 28. The two carters and George ploughing fallow in Short Lanes in the morning. I go picking up couch in the Gurze and see to the sheep before breakfast. In the afternoon the remaining piece of the Gurze is drilled with mangolds, this finishing up the mangold sowing. Mangold hoeing starts today in full swing. I drive Mrs. Venn into Horsham in the evening bringing back Grace.

Weather. Fairly bright.

Saturday May 29. In the morning I superintend three boys spudding thistles in the oats in Uptons. In the afternoon I do the same with the boys couching mangold ground in the Gurze. In the evening I prepare for taking a welcome journey homewards arriving about eight o'clock. Horses turned out nights for the first time this year.

Monday May 31. Bank Holiday.

Up at eight o'clock, have breakfast and afterwards do a little printing off of photos and set the croquet out, then do a bit of ratting. About twelve o'clock we have a swarm so am busy taking that and looking through the hives with Amy. In the afternoon we have two games of croquet, Father and I against Mother and Harold our opponents winning both games. After tea Harold and Ethel are driven into Horsham to catch the six thirty for London. I hive the swarm and return to Dial Post about eight after a most enjoyable time at home.

Weather. Glorious.

Tuesday June 1. Back again into the old routine. Moore ploughing fallow in Short Lanes, Hunt ploughing for and drilling in maize in Old Woods, about three quarters of an acre. The governor and I roll it and Hunt harrows it. In the morning I go hurdle cart with Abbey from Old Woods to Carter's field. In the afternoon we carry over the troughs, have a lot of running about and feel rather tired by evening. Work does not go down very well today.

Weather. Gloomy, but very close.

Wednesday June 2. In the morning I go cutting down nettles in the orchard and different places, afterwards having a walk round the farm with the boss. In the afternoon I go with Abbey picking up bushes round Lindfield with the horse and cart, carting them into the rick yard. Have rather a slack day it being almost a wet one.

Weather. Wet and unpleasant.

Thursday June 3. I bury Sammy before breakfast.

Up at the usual hour and sent Moore ploughing up rye ground in Old Woods. Hunt going to the station after two ton of salt in the morning and two ton of super[1] in the afternoon. In the morning Abbey and I pitch first

1 Super phosphates.

fold in the trefolium for the sheep and fetch the wool from Old Barn to Dial
Post. In the afternoon the boss and I sort out the sheep putting thirty of the
fattest into Crab Tree Croft, the others in the folium.
    Weather. Dull with cold wind.

Friday June 4.   Up at the usual time and down to the farm by myself, the
boss not caring to venture out it raining too hard. Hardly know what to set
the men at today, but the two carters go cart greasing, oiling harness, etc.
George and Lucas spar[1] making. In the morning I mend two punctures in
the governor's bike, clean up my own and mess about generally. In the
afternoon I clean up the stores and walk round to see if sheep and stock are
alright.
    Weather. Again almost a wet day.

Saturday June 5.   Set Hunt bedding up the upper yard. In the morning I
pitch two folds for the sheep and get ready for Sunday. In the afternoon
Hunt fetches two ton of coal from West Grinstead and Moore starts
clearing up where the mangold pie stood taking the rubbish into the lower
yard. In the evening I make a little duck trough for the ladies.
    Weather. Dull and close all day.

Monday June 7.   Sent the two carters to Washington after two loads of
chalk. Abbey, Steve and I are weeding in Uptons and Pond field. George
and Lucas setting out mangolds in Clapper field, Banfield starts scraping in
Hovel field. In the evening the governor and I have a walk round the farm,
seeing the hoers, etc. The governor is in a very good temper this evening,
most pleasant, getting home at eight o'clock.
    Weather. Warmer and brighter.

Tuesday June 8.   Fifteen minutes late this morning. Sent Moore ploughing
the headlands in Old Woods, Hunt cultivating fallow ground in the Gurze.
George, Lucas and Banfield hoeing in Hovel field. In the morning I pitch a
fold and do a little weeding in Pond field with Abbey and Steve. The
governor and I have tea alone today, the ladies having gone to Mrs.
Hooker's to tea. I have a chat with Burgess in the evening.
    Weather. Bright and warm.

Wednesday June 9.   Set Moore rolling, with the Cambridge, turnip ground
in the Gurze. Hunt following him with lift harrow. George, Lucas and
Abbey hoeing in Hovel field. I make a small fold for the sheep before
breakfast and a larger one afterwards. Mr. and Mrs. Crouch make a call at
Dial Post on their way to Lucerne.

1   Pointed stick used in thatching.

Weather. Dull and close.

Thursday June 10. Moore rolling fallow ground in the Gurze and Hunt following him with the iron harrows. In the afternoon Hunt uses the Parmiter harrow to tear out the couch. In the afternoon I take the weights and scales to West Grinstead to be tested. George, Abbey and Lucas hoeing in Hovel field. Banfield and Steve horse-hoeing in Clapper field and Hovel field. We have a shower of rain in the evening.
Weather. Dull and gloomy.

Friday June 11. Lucas has a holiday, George and Abbey hoeing, Moore rolling fallow in the Gurze and Hunt cultivating Short Lanes with the lift harrow. In the afternoon the boss and I have yet another go at the sheep's feet. In the afternoon Moore ploughs in a piece of maize in Old Woods rolling it and harrowing it in. I have a walk round the farm and do some horse hoeing in Clapper field, my first attempt doing several turns.
Weather. Dull and rather cold for June.

Saturday June 12. Went down to the farm with the boss and set Moore ploughing up the headlands of Carter's field. Hunt finishes cultivating Short Lanes and prepares for sowing tares in Old Woods which are put in this morning. In the afternoon George, Hunt and Moore go ploughing couched ground in the Gurze, I go horse hoeing in Clapper field before breakfast until Banfield arrives. I am hurdle carrying and pitching nearly all the rest of the day, making a large fold on the tares in Carter's field.
Weather. Very showery.

Sunday June 13. I ride my bike to Billingshurst, there being a trap full, and ride from there home, having a very pleasant time, just right for another swarm.

Monday June 14. Set the two carters and Banfield ploughing swede ground in the Gurze. Lucas setting out and finishing flat hoeing mangolds in Hovel field. George sowing salt and nitrate of soda mixed in Clapper field and also three cwt. on Rushetts. In the afternoon Hunt drags the swede ground, Moore rolling after him. The boy and I are seeing to the sheep nearly all morning. In the afternoon I have a walk round and see to the men. Mr. Venn and his brother go off to Bexhill for the day.
Weather. Fine and hot.

Tuesday June 15. Up at the usual time. Set Hunt ploughing in the Gurze, Moore rolling and Steve harrowing. George and Lucas bunching mangolds in Hovel field. In the afternoon Banfield and I go spudding thistles in the tares in the Gurze. The governor is rather cross today.

Weather. Fine and hot.

Wednesday June 16.   Hunt mowing seeds in Crab Tree field. Moore harrowing with lift harrow and then with iron harrows swede ground in Gurze.
Steve goes to market with ten sheep in a bullock cart. I pitch a fold for the
sheep and afterwards pick out the sheep with the boss and then have a fresh
job, namely knife sharpening for the mower and raking out grass from the
headland. The boss goes to Steyning market with pigs and a calf.
Weather. Fine and hot.

Thursday June 17.   Moore ploughing in the Gurze and Steve rolling swede
gound in same. Hunt finishes mowing in Crab Tree and starts cutting the
seeds in Hovel field. In the morning I pitch a fold and doctor the sheep's feet
at Old Barn and sharpen a knife. In the afternoon we drill the swedes in the
Gurze and I lead the front horse. Steve harrows behind drill. In the evening
the governor and I cotton[1] the maize which is just coming through.
Weather. Fine and very hot, thundery.

Friday June 18.   Hunt finishes cutting seeds in Hovel field and starts in Long
Lanes. Steve swath turning in the afternoon in Crab Tree field. Moore
ploughing up lucerne ground in Old Woods. I pitch a fold for the sheep in
the morning and then the governor and I go over to Old Barn after the Dutch
calf and I bring it home. In the afternoon I roll the last piece of maize put in.
Weather. Beautiful, just right for hay-making.

Saturday June 19.   Up at the usual time and set Moore ploughing lucerne
ground and Hunt continues cutting seeds in Long Lanes, Steve is slush cart,
the governor and I pitch two folds for the sheep. In the afternoon I am
messing about with the swath turner, it having gone wrong, but have to send
it up to the blacksmith's after all. After five o'clock we start carrying hay in
Crab Tree, getting up four load. I have my first experience of loading and the
governor is very pleased with same. I do not have time to get washed this
evening.
Weather. Hot.

Monday June 21.   Down to the farm with the governor. Set Moore raking.
Hunt finished cutting seeds in Long Lanes. After ten o'clock we all start on
hay cart, unloading the four loads taken up on Saturday evening. I have a
hard day's loading until eight. The governor in tugging, not a very strong
rope which breaks, falls over with a bump. Mr. and Mrs. Venn from
Somerset arrive in the evening so I am again pushed out of my room into
Kathleen's little room. Do not sleep at all well. Mr. P. Venn also arrives.

1   i.e. to cotton against the birds.

Weather. Fine.

Tuesday June 22. Set Moore ploughing up trefolium ground in Carter's field. Hunt drags turnip ground twice with heavy drags, rolls and starts harrowing with iron harrows. Steve and I are weeding in Lashmers in the morning. In the afternoon he goes horse raking in Crab Tree field. I have a look round and prepare some hurdle stakes. The governor is occupied all day in showing his two brothers round the farm. I feel rather upset when I learn that I must spend another night from my room.
Weather. Damp morning, brighter later.

Wednesday June 23. Up at the usual time, set Hunt cultivating Short Lanes with the lift harrow. Moore harrows turnip ground in the Gurze after the turnip and rape seed and artificial manure has been sown. George, Abbey and Lucas setting out[1] mangolds. I am left on my own again today the governor going to Steyning market so I have to have a walk round. In the afternoon I turn the hay rakings in Crab Tree field and some of the hay in Hovel field. The visitors depart taking Nellie with them.
Weather. Very stormy looking, but we get no rain in the day.

Thursday June 24. Up at the usual hour, down to the farm with the governor and sent the two carters to Washington after two loads of fine chalk. Lucas carting up dung in Honeypool yard the ground being too wet for setting out[1] mangolds. In the morning I see to the sheep and crack some cake and have a walk round. In the afternoon the boss and I level some stone heaps for a new road and I pitch another fold for the sheep. Owing to heavy rains haying is at a complete standstill.
Weather. Heavy storms with bright intervals.

Friday June 25. Set Hunt on cutting grass in Honeypool meadow, Moore ploughing trefolium ground in the morning and in the afternoon cultivating lucerne ground with lift harrow. After breakfast I sharpen the machine knives. In the afternoon the governor and I go over to Crab Tree Croft and mend a gap in the hedge and afterwards carry a few hurdles. The hay again has to be left untouched.
Weather. Showery morning, wet afternoon.

Saturday June 26. Set Hunt cultivating fallow in Carter's field with lift harrow, he afterwards going horse raking in Long Lanes. Moore ploughing up tare ground in Carter's field. In the morning I pitch the last fold on the tares and the firsst two on the late trefolium, then I go with the others up to Hovel field and help turn over the swaths with rakes. In the afternoon we

1 Thinning out.

Ploughing and pressing

Harrowing in seed

prepare for carrying in Hovel field but almost as soon as the waggons arrive in the field a storm comes on and we have to give it up for today.

Weather. Hot morning, stormy afternoon.

Monday June 28. Up at the usual time and set Moore ploughing tare ground in Carter's field and Hunt cultivating in same. The two Lucases setting out mangolds in the morning. In the afternoon Hunt ploughs with Moore, George and Lucas throwing up dung in Honeypool yard, having to leave the mangolds owing to heavy rain. After breakfast the governor and I go kilk[1] pulling in Hovel field. In the afternoon I pitch a fold on the trefolium and have a walk round with the boss. Hay is not touched, but is fast spoiling.

Weather. Very showery morning, better afternoon.

Tuesday June 29. Set Hunt and Moore bedding up yards with litter from the rickyards and they take up some of the rakings from Crab Tree and put in for the dry cows. In the afternoon they clear out oat cavings from Lindfield yard. After breakfast, for most of the day till four o'clock the governor, Steve and I are pulling kilk in Clapper field, after which I pitch a fold. George and Lucas casting up dung in Honeypool yard.

Weather. Wet morning, showery afternoon.

Wednesday June 30. Hunt cultivating rye ground and headlands in Old Woods and Moore clearing out Lindfield rick yard in the morning. In the afternoon the two carters, Banfield and I go turning hay in Long Lanes and Hovel fields. In the morning the governor, Banfield and I go planting cabbage in the misses in the mangold field. Steve goes to market with ten sheep but brings them back again, not fetching enough. The governor goes to market after dinner. The finish up of a rather wet month.

Weather. Much warmer and fine.

Thursday July 1. Up at the usual time and set the two carters cabbage planting in Clapper field till nine thirty. I pitch a fold and cake the sheep before breakfast. At half past nine the carters come in and we start carrying hay in Hovel field finishing it by eight o'clock taking up twelve load. I am loading all day as hard as I can go. Arrive home half past eight looking like a nigger, being smothered with dust and feeling tired. Hay dry but poor in quality. Steve turns Honeypool meadow.

Weather. Hazy and warm.

Friday July 2. Set Hunt cutting grass in Torey Mead. Moore prepares for haying. At ten o'clock we start taking up hay in Long Lanes, taking up

1 Charlock.

about nine load finishing up about six, after which I go horse raking. I have a very hard day loading and am very glad to get to bed, my feet are very tender.

Weather. Bright and hot.

Saturday July 3.   Went down to the farm with the governor and set Hunt cutting grass in Birchells which he finishes by half past four. Moore goes to Southwater station after ten sacks of oats. After ten we take up the rakings in Long Lanes and after dinner start carrying Honeypool meadow, taking up eleven load finishing about quarter to eight. I have another hard day's loading, do not get washed till nine o'clock. My feet again pain me very much. Pitched two folds before breakfast and after, one for Sunday.

Weather. Bright and hot.

Sunday July 4.   I cycle home in the morning starting about ten thirty and return eight p.m. Sid is home, we have a rare guzzle of strawberries.

Monday July 5.   Set Hunt and Steve about hay making, tedding, raking, etc. In the morning I go planting cabbage in Clapper field. In the afternoon we take up the rakings in Hovel field and Honeypool meadow. In the evening we go down and unload the two loads of rakings getting home about eight.

Weather. Fine and hot.

Tuesday July 6.   Hunt and Steve horse hoeing in Hovel field. Moore ploughing up trefolium ground in Carter's field in morning. Banfield and I go horse hoeing with the old horse hoe bought from Pack Farm sale. Owing to rain the previous night haying operations are at a standstill.

Weather. Fine morning, damp afternoon.

Wednesday July 7.   Set the two carters ploughing in Long Lanes. Steve goes to market with eleven sheep. George sows manure on the mangolds in the Gurze. Lucas and Banfield are planting cabbage in Clapper field. We pick out the sheep after breakfast, then I go out to the Gurze with manure and take some straw and hay to Dial Post. In the afternoon Abbey and I take a load of hurdles out to the Gurze and I get the sheep on to the tares. The fat sheep sell at 42s. 0d. a piece. Haying is again at an entire standstill through wet.

Weather. Heavy thunder storms with bright intervals.

Thursday July 8.   Went down to the farm with the boss and set the two carters ploughing in Long Lanes, the two Lucases hoeing in Clapper field. After breakfast Banfield and I go cabbage planting in Clapper field. In the afternoon Banfield is shaking hay with Tedder in Torey Mead and I finish taking up the rakings in Crab Tree field. Hunt goes horse hoeing in Hovel field in the afternoon.

Weather. Dull but no rain.

Friday July 9. Up a little late this morning. Did the usual shepherding. After ten o'clock we start to carry hay in Torey Mead, and for the rest of the day till nearly eight hay cart is in full swing. I am loader all day. We finish carrying the field.

Weather. Fine day, rain at night.

Saturday July 10. Moore ploughing in Long Lanes and Hunt goes to the station after two ton of linseed cake. I do a little cabbage planting in Clapper field and then the governor and I start horse hoeing the maize. In the afternoon Hunt goes tedding in Burchells and just as Banfield is about to start raking up ready for carrying we have a thunderstorm which puts a stop to all haying for the day.

Weather. Thunderstorms.

Monday July 12. Set Hunt on cutting part of Ten Acres. Moore and Abbey ploughing Long Lanes. I see to the sheep before breakfast and afterwards we attend to the first case of maggots, then the governor and I go cabbage planting in Clapper field. In the afternoon Banfield and I go cabbage planting. I have a haircut over at the carpenter's shop, one of the privileges of living in the country.

Weather. Dull, brightening up towards evening.

Tuesday July 13. A little late again this morning. Sent Hunt horse hoeing in Hovel field and Moore and Abbey ploughing in Long Lanes. About half past nine the men start on carrying in Burchells and after I have finished setting a fold I join them for the rest of the day loading. We finish Burchells, getting eleven load without rakings, not much damaged.

Weather. Stormy and just a little rain.

Wednesday July 14. Set Hunt cutting the last bit of Ten Acres, Moore and Abbey ploughing in Long Lanes. After breakfast I sharpen some knives for the machine and from half past eleven till half past five I am busy tedding the first part of Ten Acres, then I do a little pitching for the sheep. Have a busy day and am feeling rather tired.

Weather. Dull morning, bright afternoon.

Thursday July 15. Sent the two carters to Washington for two waggon load of lime ashes. In the morning I go hurdle cart, cake cracking, etc., and in the afternoon the governor and I repair the hedge between Crab Tree Croft and Crab Tree field with old hurdles. George and Lucas mowing

alongside the road and hedge mending – no hoeing or haying today. Banfield sows one cwt. of nitrate of soda on maize.
Weather. Heavy rain in morning, dull but fine afternoon.

Saturday July 17.   Written on Thursday 22nd, have been too busy to write owing to haying operations. Do not finish today till nine o'clock. Hunt starts cutting Finch's grass.
Weather. Fine.

Monday July 19.   Mr. Venn and his brother go off for the day to look at a farm so I am left in charge of haying operations. We are again very busy carrying in ten Acres taking up eleven load, everything passes off very well, thanks be unto God. I am busy horse raking and helping on the rick, getting home about nine. I see to the sheep and set a fold before breakfast. Hunt finishes cutting at Finch's.
Weather. Fine and hot.

Tuesday July 20.   Another very busy day carrying Finch's hay. I am loading all day sometimes with three pitchers and it is very windy. I think this is the hardest day's work I have yet done and I am feeling very tired and grubby by the time to leave off. Do not get home again until nearly nine. Hunt cuts Old Salts in the morning and I do the shepherding before breakfast.
Weather. Fine and very hot.

Wednesday July 21.   Another busy day carrying at Finch's. I am again busy loading all day and we finish carrying this, all except the rakings. In the evening we carry three loads from Old Salts for topping up ricks, it being rather green. Started giving the best cows a little cake.
Weather. Fine.

Thursday July 22.   Up at the usual time and set Hunt horse hoeing mangold in the Gurze and Hovel fields. Moore ploughing up the lucerne ground for the second time. I am nearly all morning seeing to the sheep. In the afternoon Banfield, Abbey and I take up the last two load of rakings from Finch's. I get home about a quarter to eight. The governor is very queer today with toothache and over-work.
Weather. Dull but fine.

Friday July 23.   I set the carters ploughing up fallow in Carter's field and afterwards in Short Lanes, the two Lucases tucking[1] and finishing off hay ricks. We finished hay making by taking up the rakings in Old Salts. The governor in bed all day.

1 Tidying up sides by plucking out loose hay.

Weather. Fine but very windy.

Saturday July 24.   I set the two carters ploughing fallow in Short Lanes, Steve and Banfield horse hoeing swedes, the two Lucases setting out swedes in the Gurze. I am all morning seeing to the sheep and pitching today's and Sunday's folds. In the afternoon I walk round and do a little to the sheep's feet. I have to pay the men in the evening. A responsibility but the Lord my God supplieth the need.
Weather. Fine and very windy.

Sunday July 25.   M. Bleriot crosses the channel in his monoplane, being the first to fly the Channel.
Weather. Stormy and rough wind.

Monday July 26.   Set two carters ploughing up fallow in Short Lanes. Banfield, Steve and Abbey hoeing mangolds in the Gurze for the third time. In the afternoon I cycle to the Vet's at Partridge Green for some liniment but find him gone, then I make a fence so that the young things can run from Crab Tree Croft into Barn field. The governor gets up after breakfast and has a walk round the farm after an absence of three days.
Weather. Stormy with bright intervals.

Tuesday July 27.   The two carters finish ploughing in Short Lanes by noon and then start cross-cutting fallow in Long Lanes. The two Lucases hoeing mangolds for third time in Hovel field, Abbey and Steve hoeing in the Gurze. In the morning I see to the sheep and finish off the hay rick at Lindfield. In the afternoon I do a little ploughing. Grace arrives for her summer holidays. Mr. and Mrs. Venn and Kathleen are gone to Horsham nearly all day.
Weather. Damp morning, wet afternoon and evening.

Wednesday July 28.   George and Lucas sowing soda on mangolds in Clapper field. Abbey and Steve thistle cutting. I see to the sheep first thing in the morning and then for a wonder I go to Steyning market with the governor returning about four o'clock. In the evening we have a walk over the farm. Very heavy fall of rain Tuesday evening and night.
Weather. Fine.

Thursday July 29.   Set the two carters ploughing fallow in Long Lanes, the two Lucases hoeing in Hovel field, Abbey and Steve hoeing maize. I do some hoeing after seeing to the sheep. Mr. and Mrs. Norman drive over for the day.
Weather. Fine.

Broadcasting

Friday July 30. Went down to the farm by myself. The governor goes off early to his brother's at Frilsham for a holiday till Monday leaving me in charge. I set the two carters ploughing in Long Lanes. Abbey, Steve and Banfield hoeing maize. In the morning I see to the sheep, do a little ploughing and prepare some stakes. In the afternoon I cycle to the policeman's to see about sheep dipping, do a little hoeing, crack some cake and look round at the stock. In the evening I drive Mrs. Venn, Grace and Kathleen over to Ashington.
Weather. Dull but fairly fine.

Saturday July 31. The two carters finish ploughing in Long Lanes then going into Carter's field cross-cutting fallow. Banfield, Abbey and Steve finish hoeing maize and go on with mangolds in the Gurze. In the morning I see to the sheep, pitching fold etc. and about eleven come in and get ready to go to the station to meet Mr. and Mrs. Martin and children. In the afternoon I pitch Sunday's fold. Everything so far going on smoothly without the gov.
Weather. Very windy, hot.

Monday August 2. Bank Holiday. Went down to the farm and set the two carters ploughing in Carter's field. Abbey, Steve and Banfield hoeing mangolds in the Gurze, Lucases hoeing in Hovel field. In the morning I see to the sheep and set a fold, then fetch a barrel of water for them. A telegram arrives from Mr. Venn to say meet him at Christ's Hospital. I drive there in the afternoon. I get within a few minutes drive of Lucerne, so near and yet so far. This has seemed a funny day.
Weather. Dull, rather cooler.

Tuesday August 3. Up at the usual time and set the two carters ploughing fallow in Carter's field. Banfield, Abbey and Steve cutting and tying rye in Old Woods. The two Lucases start thatching clover hay-rick and continue same through the day. I fetch water for the thatchers and have another go at the sheep's feet. The boss goes away again this afternoon for a sale of Dutch cattle tomorrow.
Weather. Fine.

Wednesday August 4. Set Moore ploughing in Carter's field. Hunt cultivating with lift harrow part of Carter's field and Short Lanes. Lucases finish thatching seed rick and start on meadow hay rick. Have another day on my own, see to the sheep and do a few odd jobs. *Bailiff's* wages 2s. 6d. per week.
Weather. Fine and hot.

Thursday August 5. In the morning we are all busy sheep dipping doing eighty-two. In the afternoon I drive the sheep back to the Gurze and give

them another fold. In the evening I help Hunt put together the self-binder ready for use tomorrow.
  Weather. Very hot.

Friday August 6. Went down to the farm with the boss and set Hunt on binding oats in Uptons, finishing about nine acres. Moore straw cart, and I see to the sheep in the morning and fetch water for the thatchers. I drive Mr. Norman to the station, he coming over to look at Rookland farm with Mr. Venn. The governor and Mr. Clutton settle that Mr. Norman shall have Rookland farm at Michaelmas, one hundred and twelve acres. We get no rabbits from the oats.
  Weather. Again very hot.

Saturday August 7. Hunt binding small piece of oats in Uptons and going from there to the beans in Old Woods. Moore goes to Washington after lime ashes. In the afternoon I get a barrel of water for the sheep and sharpen a knife for the binder.
  Weather. Hotter than ever, ideal for harvesting.

Sunday August 8. Tried twice to get to Billingshurst but my back tyre failed and I returned, repaired it and cycled home.

Monday August 9. Went down to the farm with the boss and set Hunt binding beans in Old Woods, which he finished and then started those in Carter's field where the connection rod breaks in the afternoon giving a full stop for today. Moore goes to Washington after lime ashes. I see to the sheep and Steve and I are nearly all day carrying some rough hay in one of the Old Barn platts.[1] In the evening I cycle to Partridge Green to see the vet and I buy a cyclometer and a bell for my bike.
  Weather. Very hot again, rather hazy.

Tuesday August 10. Set Moore ploughing tare ground in the Gurze, Hunt doing odd jobs waiting for a connecting rod which does not come, the governor has one made at Nicholls, and Hunt finishes cutting the beans in the evening. I have one journey to the station for the rod and a lot of running about in connection with the same. I change the inner tubes of my bike in the evening putting back to front and vice-versa.
  Weather. Very hot.

Wednesday August 11. Up at the usual hour and set Hunt on binding in Pond field. Moore goes to the station in the morning after a quarter ton of coal. After breakfast the governor and I pick out twelve sheep for market.

1 A piece of ground of small extent.

In the afternoon we carry rye in Old Woods putting it into Old Barn. Mr. Venn goes off to market, best sheep fetch 45*s*. 6*d*.

Weather. Another scorcher, heavy mist in morning.

Thursday August 12. Hunt finishes cutting Pond field by about ten o'clock and starts on the wheat in Oxons. Moore drives the binder at intervals, filling up his time mangold hoeing. The wheat being very tall we have rather a job to get a start. I see to the sheep before breakfast and in the morning go bean picking in Old Woods. In the afternoon I tie up missed sheaves in Oxons and do various jobs. The rest of the household going for a drive.

Weather. Still very hot, no wind.

Friday August 13. Up at the usual time and set Hunt binding in Oxons wheat which he finishes by dinner time going from there to the oats in Thistly field. In the morning I see to the sheep and go bean picking with the boys. In the afternoon I go with Banfield cutting a road round Stock Park wheat, pulling out and tying up the sheaves working until seven o'clock. Moore hoeing in Hovel field. I am obliged to have a new tyre on the back wheel of my bike.

Weather. Not quite so hot but hot enough.

Saturday August 14. Down to the farm with the boss and set Hunt binding part of Thistly field which he finishes by one o'clock and then he makes a start on Stock Park wheat. Moore hoeing in Hovel field. I am seeing to the sheep nearly all day, making Sunday's fold and fetching water, etc. I had thought to have a week-end now, Sid being home, but cannot owing to the governor going to Mr. Burden's funeral tomorrow afternoon. I have another mop[1] in the carpenter's shop.

Weather. Very hot and terribly muggy evening.

Monday August 16. Set Hunt on cutting wheat in Stock Park which he finished by one o'clock afterwards cutting the remainder of the oats in Uptons. Moore ploughing up rye ground in Old Woods. Mr. S. Venn arrives at dinner time and they both go off at dinner time to look at a farm. I get home to an early tea and then drive the Martins to the station who are returning to London after a fortnight's stay here.

Weather. Dull, little rain much cooler.

Tuesday August 17. Went down to the farm and sent the two carters to Washington after two waggon load of lime ashes. The two Lucases tying up straw and cutting a road round Eight acres, boys thistle bobbing. I see to

1 Haircut.

the sheep and afterwards Abbey and I are taking out and tying up wheat in Lashmers after Banfield, who cut a road round. I am feeling very happy today somehow.

Weather. Fine morning, gentle rain during evening.

Wednesday August 18. Up at the usual time, set Moore ploughing tare ground in the Gurze, Hunt ploughing rye ground in Old Woods. After breakfast the governor and I pick out twelve sheep for market, four of which return, the trade being worse than ever, the remainder fetching 42s. 0d. and 43s. 0d. Manna and her friend arrive at Dial Post. Banfield and Lucases trimming hedge alongside the farm road.

Weather. Very heavy storms.

Thursday August 19. Hunt binding wheat and wheat and oats mixed in Lashmers. Moore ploughs in the Gurze and rye ground in Old Woods. I see to the sheep before breakfast. They get out through the hedge into Crab Tree Croft and wander onto a neighbouring farm, so that I have a long tramp before I could find them. I do some ploughing and ride round two or three turns on the binder. We have some sport in the afternoon and evening killing eighteen rabbits.

Weather. Stormy, but we get little rain.

Friday August 20. Set Hunt cutting oats in Lashmers which he has to leave owing to rain. Moore harrowing rye ground in Old Woods for mustard, harrowing it in after Banfield who sows it. Afterwards they all go carting lime on to Short Lanes. The governor and I go to a sale at Ellen's Green Rudgwick calling in Lucerne to tea on our way back just in time to see Mother and Father start off for a holiday to Rothsay for seventeen days.

Weather. Almost a wet day very miserable.

Saturday August 21. Up at the usual time, set Hunt ploughing and the two Lucases on lime cart in Short Lanes which they finish at noon. Moore goes to Washington for a load of big chalk. After dinner Hunt finishes cutting oats in Lashmers and starts on Eight Acres. I see to the sheep, making Sunday's fold etc. In the afternoon I go setting up fallen down sheaves. In the evening I go a few rounds on the binder bumpty, bumpty, bump, as if I was riding my charger oh my poor B.T.M.

Weather. Fairly bright with a little rain.

Monday August 23. Set Hunt cutting oats in Eight Acres, which he finishes and starts on Rushetts but has to leave off on account of rain coming on. We start carrying oats in Uptons, get up three loads when rain prevents more progress. For the rest of the day all hands are dung cart from Honeypool to Carter's field. I have my first experience of loading sheaves. Have a postcard from Mother saying they had arrived at Rothsay safely.

Weather. Fine morning wet afternoon and evening.

Tuesday August 24. All hands on dung cart to fallow in Carters field. I see to the sheep and help Banfield set up blown down shocks in Uptons. In the afternoon Hunt starts cutting in Rushetts but has to leave off after two rounds owing to rain. Banfield and I cut out dodder[1] patches in clover in Crab Tree. Moore and Steve go hurdle cart from the Gurze to tares and rape in Old Woods.

Weather. Another wet miserable afternoon and evening.

Wednesday August 25. Set Hunt cultivating in Long Lanes and Moore goes to the station after two ton of linseed cake. In the morning and afternoon Banfield and I are cutting out dodder patches in Crab Tree. The sheep are turned out to grass it being so wet and dirty, so do not have much to do to them today. The governor goes to market with three calves.

Weather. Stormy and we get very heavy thunderstorms about two o'clock a lot of mud about today.

Thursday August 26. Up at the usual time. Hunt goes cultivating in Long Lanes with lift barrow. Moore ploughs tare ground in the Gurze. The governor goes to a sale at Westlands staying all day. In the morning I have a look round at the oats which are growing rather. In the afternoon Hunt goes cutting oats in Rushetts. I put the sheep on to the rape and tares in Old Woods and look round to see the cutting. My 'little Mary' feels a bit queer in the afternoon. I have to sit down a bit, and it passes off.

Weather. Rather dull but not any rain.

Friday August 27. Went down to the farm with the boss and set Hunt on cutting in Rushetts. Moore finishes ploughing the tare ground in the Gurze and starts on the Old Woods headlands, in the afternoon he goes drag harrowing in tare ground. In the afternoon I go picking up hedge trimmings around Old Woods with Steve. In the evening I go picking plums for the ladies for jam making.

Weather. Fine at last, fairly bright.

Saturday August 28. Set Hunt on cutting in Rushetts which he finishes and starts on Tenchford. Moore goes to the station after ten sacks of oats. I see to the sheep and help Banfield cutting out dodder patches in Crab Tree clover. In the afternoon Moore ploughs headlands in Old Woods, the

---

1 A slender leafless plant, like masses of twining threads, parasitic on clover.

governor and I go setting up fallen sheaves in Pond and Thistly fields. After
tea I finish pitching for Sunday and gather some greengages for Mrs. Venn.
Hunt finishes cutting wheat in Tenchford, thus finishing this year's corn
cutting, no carrying today.
    Weather. Fine.

Sunday August 29. I cycle to Billingshurst in the morning. In the evening
we all go to Ashington. Today has been to me a real time of happiness with
my Lord. Oh that there were more Sabbaths like this one has been. Praise
the Lord.

The next five entries are written diagonally across the page and lack the
usual detail as harvest cart goes on till eight o'clock most evenings.

Monday August 30. Busy all day as hard as we can go carrying Oxon's
wheat, finishing the field, twenty two waggon load. I am loading sheaves
all day. Knock off at eight o'clock.

Tuesday August 31. Again very busy carrying wheat in Stock Park, getting
eighteen load. I am again hard at it loading, feeling very tired by eight
o'clock. We finish this field and start in Uptons.
    Weather. The last two days fine.

Wednesday September 1. Another day's carrying in Uptons and Thistly
fields. We are stopped at five o'clock by rain leaving about six load in
Thistly field. Am rather glad of an early evening.
    Weather. Fine, damp evening.

Thursday September 2. Another hard day's carrying. We carry Tenchford
wheat, finish off Thistly field and Uptons and get a waggon load of beans
up in Old Woods. I am very busy loading all day and seeing to the sheep.
Knock off time eight o'clock. We have a frost in the early morning, quite
sharp.
    Weather. Fine and hot.

Friday September 3. Yet another busy day carrying. We carry two loads of
beans from Old Woods, clear Pond field with fourteen load and get four
load from Rushetts. I see to the sheep before breakfast and for the rest of the
day till eight o'clock am busy loading.
    Weather. Could not be better.

Saturday September 4. We are carrying beans all the morning from Old
Woods and Carter's field getting six load from Old Woods and three from
Carter's field. It comes on to rain at dinner time so that carrying is stopped

for today. In the afternoon the two carters plough in Uptons for trefolium. All the beans are put into Old Barn. Another visitor arrives, by name Kathleen Garrard. The finish up of a very busy week of hard graft.

Weather. Fine morning damp afternoon and evening.

Monday September 6.   Down to the farm and set the two carters and Abbey ploughing in Uptons for trefolium. The Lucases start thatching the corn ricks. I see to the sheep in the morning and doctor some of their feet. In the afternoon Banfield and I pack up the wool ready for rail. In the evening we carry four loads of wheat from Lashmers to Lindfield barn. Dearest Mother and Father return to Lucerne after seventeen days holiday in Scotland, may the blessing of the Lord rest upon them.

Weather. Showery morning wet afternoon.

Tuesday September 7.   Up at the usual time and set all hands carrying oats from Rushetts. We finish this field getting nineteen load and get a few load from Eight Acres. In the evening we take up two loads of wheat from Lashmers when rain comes on and prevents further progress. Spend a pleasant evening indoors playing Quit.

Weather. Fine day, damp evening.

Wednesday September 8.   Set Hunt rolling and Moore harrowing trefolium ground in Uptons. Banfield sows the seed with barrow and Moore harrows after. Both early and late are put in today. We go harvest cart in the afternoon finishing off Eight Acres in the evening when rain comes on. I do a little work with the seed barrow in the morning and in the afternoon am busy loading sheaves. Mabel and Doris leave today for their homes. Ten sheep are sent to market but five are brought back, the highest bid for them being 34s. 0d., the others making 40s. 0d. Eight Acres yields fifteen loads.

Weather. Very cold first thing, fine day and damp evening.

Thursday September 9.   The two carters go to the station twice for eight tons of lindseed cake. I see to the sheep and the men before breakfast and in the morning the governor and I pick out fifteen sheep for fattening on grass. In the afternoon Banfield, Steve and I set up the sheaves again in Lashmers and in the evening we carry one and a half loads of wheat and put it into Lindfield barn. Mr. and Mrs. Venn go to Shoreham after dinner and return about eight thirty p.m., both seem rather bad tempered on their return.

Weather. Fine.

Friday September 10.   Set Moore ploughing trefolium ground in Uptons, which he finishes and starts ploughing up bean ground in Carter's field. Hunt goes to the station in the morning after two ton of coal and in the

Mowing grass for hay

Hay cart

afternoon drags the remainder of tare ground in the Gurze. I am pottering about all day doing various jobs and going over part of the farm with the governor. In the evening I mend a puncture for him. Nothing done towards harvest today.
Weather. Wet first thing, afterwards stormy.

Saturday September 11. Went down to the farm with the governor and set the two carters ploughing bean ground in Carter's field. About three o'clock we have a terrific thunderstorm so am obliged to turn out the sheep till evening. Faggot cart in the morning and in the afternoon I shift the mixed corn sheaves in Lashmers on to fresh ground in order to keep the clover alive and prepare Sunday's folds. Nellie returns today from Frilsham.
Weather. Fairly fine.

Monday September 13. The two carters ploughing in Carter's field for wheat. Banfield goes ploughing bean ground in Old Woods for wheat where the two carters join him after dinner. In the afternoon the boss and I have a walk round the farm, he is in a very good temper. This is the sort of day when farming is 'not all honey'. Mud again begins to make its appearance.
Weather. Almost a wet day, very miserable.

Tuesday September 14. One of the pleasures of being a farm pupil is that sometimes you do not get your bed made as mine has not been today.
Went down to the farm and set the two carters and Banfield ploughing for wheat in Old Woods. I see to the sheep before breakfast and about ten o'clock the governor and I drive down to Findon Fair, staying there till about half past two, there being a great many lambs and ewes there, the price of good store lambs ranging from 30s. 0d. to 35s. 0d. and ewes about 37s. 0d. In the evening we have a look round the day's work Mr. Venn in a very good temper again. I feel so thankful that I am learning to be a farmer, what could be better.
Weather. Drying wind and fine.

Wednesday September 15. Set all hands on dung cart from the cow stall yard on to Carter's field. In the morning I am picking pears, helping to load the wool and turning rakings. In the afternoon I pull over the remaining wheat shocks in Lashmers and some of the oats and burn up a heap of hedge trimmings in Carter's field. The governor goes to Steyning market bringing home two Dutch bull calves from Strivens, Little Buckingham Farm. In the evening I am working till eight o'clock helping take up the wheat rakings. Lucases finish thatching corn ricks today.
Weather. Fine.

Thursday September 16.   Set all hands carting dung from the stable yard on to the mixen. The gov. goes off by the ten o'clock train to Croydon to see about renewing the milk contract. Very dirty getting about and I am obliged to turn the sheep out.
Weather. Damp morning, finer afternoon.

Friday September 17.   Up at the usual time and set all hands on dung cart from the cow yard on to Short Lanes. I see to the sheep before breakfast and in the morning the governor and I again set up the sheaves which were thrown down in Lashmers. In the afternoon we repair the hedge between Stock Park and Cottage Meadow. Grace comes back from London today having secured a post. Mrs. Venn rather ill-tempered today.
Weather. Fine and warm.

Saturday September 18.   Set the men on dung cart to Short Lanes. In the morning I see to the sheep and prepare Sunday's fold, and do the old job of foot-rot cure. In the afternoon the governor and I see to drying some of the sheaves in Lashmers and in the evening we finish carrying the wheat and take up half load of oats. The servant goes away today for a week-end so in the evening the boss and I toss up as to who shall light the fire in the morning, of course the poor lodger falls a victim, no rest for the weary.
Weather. Fine and warm.

Monday September 20.   The two carters go to the station for coal in the morning. I see to the sheep before breakfast and then go throwing down sheaves in Lashmers. We go harvest cart from Lashmers in the afternoon and evening, thus finishing up the harvest for this year. I load the last load and am very glad to finish off at last. Our servant came home from a week-end's holiday yesterday very ill and is in bed all day today.
Weather. Fine and hot.

Tuesday September 21.   Went down to the farm with the governor and sent Hunt to the station twice after coal. Moore and George go ploughing for wheat in Old Woods. Lucas, Abbey and Steve fag[1] the small piece of tares for seed in the Gurze. The governor goes to a sale at Griggs farm and buys three cows and some heifers. I am burning up rubbish nearly all day, hedge trimmings, etc., and have my hair cut in the evening by Moore. Mr. Venn comes home very queer from the sale.
Weather. Fine.

Wednesday September 22.   Up at the usual time and set the carters ploughing for wheat in Old Woods. The two Lucases dung spreading in Carter's field.

1   Fag – by hand, with fag hook or swap hook.

After breakfast we pick out six sheep and I take them to Steyning market in the milk cart and bring back two calves which the governor buys. Sheep fetch three at 41s. 0d. and three at 43s. 0d. The stock is fetched home from yesterday's sale.

Weather. Fine except for a little rain in the afternoon.

Thursday September 23. Set the two carters on ploughing in dung in Carter's field for wheat. The two Lucases dung spreading. The boss and I attend to one or two of the sheep in the morning and drive them into Ten Acres, they having finished the cabbage, thus ending this year's folding. In the afternoon I take some troughs up to Ten Acres and do some dung spreading. I again help with various things indoors, nothing like getting your hand in.

Weather. Rather a wet morning, fine afternoon.

Friday September 24. All hands dung cart to Short Lanes in the morning. In the morning I am running about with letters and a wire for Manna with regard to a post. In the afternoon the two carters plough in dung in Carter's field. I help Banfield pick up potatoes. Have a bit of a lark with the girls in the evening. Manna and I are locked out, but our merriment is short lived for it upsets the governor, so that we have to retire to bed rather solemnly.

Weather. Fine with a little rain in the afternoon.

Saturday September 25. Set the two carters and George ploughing fallow in Carter's field for wheat, all the rest of the hands finish dung spreading in Carter's field and start in Short Lanes. In the afternoon I look round the ploughing, etc. The governor goes off in the morning to try and secure extra milk contract for twenty – thirty gallons and is successful. I cycle over to Lucerne in the evening till Sunday night, arriving about a quarter to eight. Sid and Amy come to meet me.

Weather. Variable, heavy showers.

Sunday September 26. Spend a most happy day with my loved ones, 'tis hard to have to depart from them.

Monday September 27. Back to the old routine of work. Set the two carters and George ploughing fallow for wheat in Carter's field. All the other hands dung spreading in Short Lanes. The governor goes off to Shoreham to see Mr. Norman by the half past seven train, saying he will be back about ten a.m. but does not do so till eight o'clock. In the morning I am turning tares, burning rubbish and taking hay and straw to Dial Post. In the afternoon I have a look at the ploughing and do some burning.

Weather. Fine.

Tuesday September 28.   Two carters and George ploughing, the rest dung spreading. I see to the sheep before breakfast and afterwards drive Mr. Venn, Manna and Kathleen into Horsham, occupying most of the day. In the evening I have a long chat with Old Johnson on spiritual matters and also Burgess on same. I feel how little I know when confronted with various questions. Oh that I knew more of the Word.

Weather. A wet miserable day.

Wednesday September 29.   Up at the usual time and sent Hunt to Washington after a waggon load of chalk. The two Lucases filling up holes in rick-yard and Moore littering up cow yard. I see to the despatch of three cows to Steyning market, and the threshing tackle comes in so have to see to that in the morning. The governor goes to Horsham in the morning and from there to Steyning and buys two cows, one calf and two rams and is away all day.

Weather. A regular wet day, floods out.

Thursday September 30.   This month there have been sixteen days fine and fourteen with rain.

Went over to Rookland farm to fetch over Cheesemore for threshing, have a look round and then come back to see to the sheep. Hunt goes to Washington after a waggon load of lime. All the other hands busy with the threshing. I have a busy day pitching straw on the straw rick. From today's rick we get one hundred and nineteen sacks. The seventy ewes come from Mr. Norman. Spend a very pleasant evening indoors, every one seems to be in a good temper. Yet another month has rolled away. Rams put to ewes.

Weather. Fine but very dirty underfoot.

Friday October 1.   Hunt to Washington after a waggon load of lime ashes. All the other hands threshing oats at Lindfield in the morning. Banfield and I cycle over to Steyning after a cow. Wheat threshing is finished about one o'clock getting thirty nine sacks (Lashmers wheat). Banfield, the governor and I are fencing in Crab Tree Croft in the afternoon. The two Lucases straw-tying, Moore doing odd jobs.

Weather. Damp first thing, fine after.

Saturday October 2.   Set Hunt cutting clover seed in Crab Tree Croft. Moore goes to Washington after lime ashes. The two Lucases are mowing in Crab Tree Croft and also the piece in Long Lanes. In the morning Cheesemore and myself are busy shifting stock etc. from Dial Post to Rookland. In the afternoon I sharpen a knife and have a go at the sheep's feet. Shall I ever cure foot-rot?

Weather. Much better, quite hot at times.

Sunday October 3.   Have a long jaunt from seven to after ten after sheep, find them at last but get wet through. To Ashington in evening with Manna and Kathleen, have a harvest thanksgiving service.

Monday October 4.   Did the usual before breakfast duties of caking the sheep. Moore goes to the station in the morning after two ton of cotton cake. Hunt goes cleaning stubble in Rushetts with lift harrow. Abbey finishes dung spreading in Short Lanes. The two Lucases hedge mending and trimming. After breakfast the governor rides the pony over to Butterstock's sale. I go round and tell the men what to do and then cycle over to the sale, spending the day there.
   Weather. Showery, cannot seem to get anything but wet.

Tuesday October 5.   Set Hunt cultivating stubble in Rushetts with Mrs. Hooker's Massey-Harris cultivator. Moore finishes clearing out stable yard filling it up again with the hedge trimmings and oat cavings[1] having Abbey to help. The others hedge trimming. The governor goes to Haywards Heath market. I drive him to the station and look over Rookland in the afternoon. Have a fairly easy day.
   Weather. Very showery morning, finer afternoon.

Wednesday October 6.   Went down to the farm by myself, the boss going off to Chichester market early. Send the two carters over to Rookland to plough oat stubble for wheat. The two Lucases shoot out the wheat in the stores, then they and the other hands go hedge trimming. In the afternoon they turn the clover seed in Long Lanes. I run over to Rookland to see the ploughing after breakfast, then go down to the farm and pick out six sheep for market which I drive down in the milk cart. They are sold privately for 42s. 6d. a piece. I meet Mr. Venn there and we return early and take up the clover seed in Long Lanes, two half loads.
   Weather. A bright day which is a real treat.

Thursday October 7.   Hunt cutting seed clover in Hovel field in the morning. Moore goes ploughing oat stubble over at Rookland. I see to the sheep before breakfast, then do some bullock driving and afterwards myself and all hands go turning clover seed in Crab Tree and in the afternoon take up two and a half load, when rain comes on and stops further progress.
   Weather. Fine till four o'clock when rain comes on and we have a very rough evening.

Friday October 8.   White frost.

1 Husks left after threshing.

Did not wake up till six twenty so had to go without a wash. Sent the two carters to finish oat stubble at Rookland which they do by one o'clock. In the afternoon I take the winnowing machine back to Mr. Sewards and bring our away. George is hedge trimming. Lucas gap stopping. Mr. and Mrs. Venn have a row at dinner time and Mrs. Venn leaves the table going upstairs.
    Weather. Fine and windy.

Saturday October 9.   White frost.
    Sent the two carters to the station after five ton of super. About ten o'clock we all go turning clover in Crab Tree with rakes and after dinner the carters come out and we start carrying and take up all that is fit, namely four load. I am loader. Rain comes on again in the evening. I am very glad it is Saturday night again.
    Weather. Fine and quite hot.

Monday October 11.   Sent the carters to the station for ten ton of basic slag, each going twice. Lucas mending gaps in hedges. George sows salt on leigh in Long Lanes and then goes hedge trimming. In the morning Banfield and I are driving calves and heifers over to Rookland. In the afternoon Mr. Venn, George, Steve and myself go turning seed clover in Crab Tree but it is of little use as the rain comes on and we have a wet evening.
    Weather. Showery.

Tuesday October 12.   Sent the carters after another ten ton of basic slag, each going twice. I see to the sheep before breakfast and afterwards go to the mill at Partridge Green with nine bushels of pig corn to be ground. In the afternoon George, Lucas, Steve and myself go turning seed clover in Hovel field. Another maid arrives today being the fourth during my residence at Dial Post. I have felt very happy today somehow.
    Weather. Variable with some showers.

Wednesday October 13.   Up at the usual time. Set the two carters ploughing lea in Long Lanes. Steve pressing after them. Having had a very high wind without rain last night the clover seed is ready to carry by half past eight but just as the men get to the field to rake it in, a heavy storm comes on and prevents further progress. In the afternoon the carters go caving cart into the stable yard. Lucas winnowing wheat. I help get in the maize for the cows and see to the sheep, otherwise there is very little doing today. A plentiful supply of mud prevails.
    Weather. Wet morning, fine afternoon.

Thursday October 14.   Set Hunt and Banfield ploughing lea in Long Lanes. Moore goes to Steyning after ten sacks of wheat from Mr. Norman's. I help pull and load turnips for the cows before breakfast and afterwards stop gaps between Old Woods and Crab Tree fields, till about eleven o'clock, then for the rest of the day am turning seed clover. We take up half a load from Crab Tree in the afternoon. This is valuation day at Rooklands so the gov. is away in the afternoon.

Weather. Fine, only a few spots of rain today.

Friday October 15.   A little late this morning, set the two carters ploughing in Long Lanes, do a good bit of ploughing with Hunt in the morning. In the afternoon I clean up the granary and help George and Lucas put the cloths on the clover rick to rights. Mr. Venn goes off to a sale at West Chiltington and buys another horse for £13. His brother goes off early in the morning, takes my bike saying not a word to me. Nothing like plenty of cheek.

Weather. Same as ever, wet and miserable rough winds.

Saturday October 16.   The two carters picking up hedge trimmings. The two Lucases hedge trimming. After breakfast Banfield and I take a horse and dung cart and go over to the sale at West Chiltington and bring back the purchased lots including Ralli cart[1] and mare. I drive back in the trap. Have a very wet miserable ride, drizzly rain all the way, Work at a standstill, everything sodden.

Weather. Wet, wet and still more wet, drizzly driving rain continues all day.

Sunday October 17.   I drive Mr. Venn, Kathleen and Manna to Ashington. Sundays are far too short for me.

Monday October 18.   Went down to the farm with the boss and set the two carters clearing up round Honeypool and carting rubbish into the yard. In the afternoon they cart cavings on to Nine Corners from Lindfield yard. The two Lucases making up cart shed floor and hedge trimming. In the morning I take some corn to the mill and bring the ground back. The governor goes over to Mr. Norman's in the afternoon. Am feeling well and lively today.

Weather. Fine, a welcome change.

Tuesday October 19.   Twenty minutes late this morning. Set the two carters ploughing lea in Long Lanes. In the afternoon Hunt goes cutting clover seed in Hovel field while Moore finishes off in Long Lanes. In the morning I am helping Banfield load hedge trimmings and sharpen two machine knives. In the afternoon I carry up some hurdles to Ten Acres and make a small pen and litter it up with straw and try some new foot rot cure. The governor goes to Haywards Heath market, his brother departs.

---

1   A form of light two-wheeled trap for four persons – named after first purchaser.

Wednesday October 20.   The men go carrying seed clover in Hovel field, get one load when rain again prevents progress. Afterwards the two carters and George go ploughing top part of Uptons for wheat. Lucas and Steve hedging. I turn the ewes over to Crab Tree after breakfast and then get the milk cart ready to take six sheep to market, then the governor and I pick them out and we both drive down to Steyning. They sell today for 42*s*. 0*d*. Have to have a light to get up by this morning.

Weather. Most of the day wet, very heavy rain at times.

Thursday October 21.   Send the two carters to the station after five ton of bone meal. In the morning Banfield, Cheesemore and I unload the two loads of seed clover and top up the rick. I crack some cake and cart it up Lindfield and do some more of the sheep's feet. Mr. Norman comes in the morning and stays till after tea. The two Lucases start mangold pulling in Crab Tree. A splendid crop.

Weather. Fairly fine with some showers.

Friday October 22.   Set the two carters ploughing in Uptons. The two Lucases thatching seed clover rick, other hands hedge trimming. Banfield joins the carters at plough. In the morning I do some ploughing, Moore feels very queer so I give him a bit of a rest. Mr. Venn goes over to see Mr. Norman. We have a fowl for dinner which I have to carve, nothing like gaining experience. The threshing tackle arrives, also Mr. S. Venn.

Weather. Fine till night when rain comes on.

Saturday October 23.   Up at the usual time. Set the men on carting out the dung from Old Barn yard on to Torey Mead. I see to the sheep before breakfast and afterwards look round at the work and then kill an incurable sheep and try to skin it, but alas after much hacking and pulling I leave it until I get some of the governor's help. In the afternoon I dig its grave, 'alas my poor brother', and do various jobs. Mr. Venn goes to court for his straying heifer is fined 1*s*. 0*d*. and 5*s*. 0*d*. costs. Heifers from Mr. Norman's arrive.

Weather. Wet first thing, finer later.

Monday October 25.   Set Moore ploughing in Uptons, all the other hands threshing. I see to the sheep before breakfast and for the rest of the day I am busy with the threshing, pitching sheaves in the barn amongst the dust, the result being an itchy head in the evening. Out of Honeypool barn we get one hundred and forty-two sacks running out to about six quarter an acre. The governor goes to Horsham in the afternoon. Casuals are on mangold pulling.

Weather. Clear and colder.

Tuesday October 26. Down to the farm with the boss and set Moore and Abbey clearing heap of muck at Lindfield on to the meadow. Hunt and Steve picking up the hedge trimmings. George and Lucas start on mangold pulling but rain stops them and they come into the stores winnowing oats, the boss and I helping them. In the afternoon the two carters and Steve also come in. I have another spiritual chat with Mr. and Mrs. Burgess in the evening.

Weather. A heavy downpour continues all day. I have never before seen so much water about. Will the rain ever cease. 'Have faith in God the sun will shine.'

Wednesday October 27. Sent Hunt over to Rookland with a waggon load of straw and Moore with cake and cake crusher and sheep troughs, etc. Afterwards they go littering up the yards. I help winnow some oats in the morning with the two Lucases and Banfield. In the afternoon the Lucases go mangold pulling but rain stops them at four o'clock. I drive the thirty-nine fat sheep over to Rookland. Nine bullocks are tied up for fattening. The governor and his brother go off to Steyning market after dinner.

Weather. Wet, raining little or much all day coming on fast toward evening. Floods very high.

Thursday October 28. Set all hands on carting beans from Old Barn to thresher at Honeypool. We thresh five load getting twenty sacks. I am loading nearly all the morning, a very dusty job. In the afternoon Banfield and I go over to Steyning on our bikes after two cows and calves bought at the market. I feel rather queer today as if I have a cold coming but it passes off in the evening and I feel alright. Get rather mud begrimed today.

Weather. Wake up today to find the same old sort, rain, rain, rain, it spatters nearly all day coming on heavy in the evening. Cold wind.

Friday October 29. Down to the farm and set the two carters carting oats bought by Mr. Hoar over to Rookland for storage. I go over with one waggon, come back and help winnow some oats in the morning. In the afternoon the carters are littering up yards, etc. Steve and I are carting swedes from the Gurze to Lindfield. Oh dear, the mud, never before did I get about in so much or get so splashed and dirty. My coat falls off the horses' hames[1] into a ditch full of water and mud and is run over by the cart coming out all mud begrimed and wet, farming isn't without its pleasures.

Weather. Brighter and colder.

---

1 Each of two curved pieces of wood or metal placed over, fastened to, or forming, the collar of a draught horse.

after dinner
    Weather wet, raining little or much all day, coming on fast
toward evening. Floods very high.

SUN RISES 6.48
SUN SETS 4.49.   **28** THURSDAY (301-64)
                            O Full Moon 10.7 p.m.
    Casuals mangel pulling.   9 Bullocks tied up at Rookland.
Up at the usual time. Went down to the farm with Mr Venn
and set all hands on carting beans from Old Barn to the
thrasher at Honeypool. he thrash five load getting 20 sacks. I am
loading nearly all the morning, a very dusty job. In the afternoon Banfield + I go over to Steyning on our bikes after
two cows and calves, bought at the market. I feel rather queer today, as if I have a cold coming, but it passes off in the evening
+ I feel alright. Get rather mud begrimed to-day

    Weather. wake up to-day to find the same old sort, rain, rain
rain, it spatters nearly all day, coming on heavy in the evening cold.

                    29 FRIDAY (302-63)
            Casuals mangel pulling
Up at the usual time Went down to the farm and set the
carters, carting oats bought by Mr Foar, over to Rookland
for storage. I go over with one waggon, come back and help
winnow some oats, in the morning. In the afternoon the carters
are littering up yards etc: Steve and I are carting swedes
from th Gorse to Findfield. Oh dear the mud, never before did
I get about in so much, or get so splashed and dirty. My coat
falls off the horses haimes into a ditch full of water and mud
+ is run over by the cart, coming out all mud begrimed + wet, farming isn't without its pleasure. Weather, brighter + colder.

                    30 SATURDAY (303-62)

Up at the usual time. Went down to the farm with
the boss, and set all hands on mangel cart in Clapper
field. The ground is very soft, the carts cutting in terribly
obliged to use a trace horse each time. I am uncovering heaps
in the morning, + turn the ewes over to Rookland. I finish
for the day at dinner time. Afterwards I get ready for a
cycle run to Worthing, this being the start of a weeks holiday
Sid meets me on the way, and we arrive at Worthing, or rather
at Mr Billets in time for tea. Have a run round the town
in the evening. It is quite nice to get a holiday.   X
            Weather. fine.

Facsimile page from the diary

Saturday October 30. Up at the usual time, set all hands on mangld cart in Clapper field. The ground is very soft, the carts rutting in terribly, obliged to use a trace horse each time. I am uncovering heaps in the morning and turn the ewes over to Rookland. I finish for the day at dinner time. Afterwards I get ready for a cycle run to Worthing this being the start of a week's holiday. Sid meeting me on the way and we arrive at Mrs. Millets, Sid's lodging, in time for tea. Have a run round the town in the evening. It is quite nice to get a holiday.
Weather. Fine.

Sunday October 31. Go to the Tabernacle in the morning and evening and Bible class in the afternoon. Days with rain twenty, without, eleven this month.

Monday November 1. Have breakfast about eight o'clock, then Sid packs his portmanteau. We cycle over to Durrington to see Capel who shows us round the nursery and after spending a little time there we return to Worthing for dinner. After dinner we prepare for a move homewards, going round to Miss Skinner's after rent and after a seemingly long wearing ride arrive at Lucerne for tea about five. Spend the evening round the fire. Tis good go be home once more with dear ones.
Weather. Fine.

Tuesday November 2. Start the day with breakfast just after eight o'clock. Sid and I drive Girlie into Horsham to fetch his portmanteau. In the afternoon we cycle to the Bungalow, Slinfold which is empty and have a good look round. Father goes to Horsham and buys a lot of privet for the front hedge. Spent a quiet evening indoors.
Weather. Fine.

Wednesday November 3. (Cows taken in at night.)
Get up to eight o'clock breakfast and then Father drives Sid and I to Slinfold station and we start off by the nine o'six for a day in London, arriving at London Bridge about a quarter to eleven. From there we have a bus ride to Spencers and are each measured for suits and knickers. From there we go to Lyons and have dinner and then make our way to St. George's Hall for Maskeylyne and Devant's performance where we spend the afternoon. After coming from there we have tea at Lyons and make our way towards Victoria and before starting for home have a little snack at the ABC. We arrive home about nine thirty. A very enjoyable day.
Weather. Rather misty in town but fine.

Thursday November 4. Eight o'clock breakfast, Sid and I go puncture mending in my bike after breakfast and then he puts the saddle on Girlie and

I ride her down to Mr. Collins to have her clipped, going from there into Horsham with a pair of trousers to be shortened, and walking home. I have a game of bagatelle in the evening and I strike a bargain with Sid for his brown suit at 35s. 0d.

Weather. Fine, frosty.

Friday November 5. In the morning Sid and I start forking up the front shrubbery and cut dead wood out of oak trees. Rhubarb wine partaken of at eleven. Mother and Father go to Horsham after dinner to meet May and from there to Warnham. Sid and I cycle to meet them.

Weather. Fine.

Saturday November 6. Sid and myself have a general clear up and in company with Father have discussions on general improvements. At eleven o'clock we make our way to the kitchen after Rhubarb wine and are handed a two gallon jar full to which we help ourselves (Rule Britannia).

Weather. Frosty and fine.

Sunday November 7. Mother, Sid and I go to Broadbridge Heath in the evening, Sid taking the meeting, have a very good time.

Fresh cowman (Norman) starts at Dial Post.

Monday November 8. I return from my week's holiday, arriving about half past twelve. Tis hard to have to leave one's dear ones and makes one long for that day when parting shall be no more, to be for ever with the Lord. In the afternoon I am helping with the mangold cart in Hovel field loading, etc. – not quite so good as holiday making. In the evening the governor and I go down and dress some wheat for sowing tomorrow. Start wheat sowing today by putting in four and a half acres at Rookland.

Weather. Frosty and fine.

Tuesday November 9. It seems rather against the grain to get up at six this morning after eight o'clock rising for a week. All the hands go mangold cart Hovel field this morning. I am helping load from just after seven, keeping at it all day, making my back ache rather and stiff generally. In the afternoon George sows wheat in Long Lanes. Hunt harrowing in after him.

Weather. Frosty and fine.

Wednesday November 10. Set all hands except Hunt and George mangold cart in Hovel field. Hunt and George putting in wheat in piece of lea in Long Lanes. I am busy with the mangolds all day. Mr. Venn goes to market with five sheep, they fetch 45s. 0d. George and Hunt put in French wheat in small piece of Carter's field. In the evening we go down and dress some more wheat till nearly eight o'clock. Finish off mangold pie in Hovel field.

Weather. Fine, cold wind.

Thursday November 11. Set George and Hunt sowing wheat in Carter's field, Steve harrowing in. The other hands mangold cart in Hovel field, carting them into the barn. I help throw up first and then I take up driving between so have a fairly easy day today. Have a very cheering letter from Sid this morning. He is a dear old chap.
Weather. Frosty and fine.

Friday November 12. Up at the usual time and set George and Hunt wheat sowing in Carter's field. Moore and Lucas wheat-sowing over at Rookland on the piece of fallow. In the morning before breakfast we dress some wheat and afterwards Abbey and myself go mangold cart from Hovel field to Lindfield and Dial Post. I take some wheat to Rookland and in the afternoon Abbey and myself go mangold carting into Rookland barn, taking in nine load. George starts dirting up mangold pies in Crab Tree.
Weather. Rather more dull, but fine.

Saturday November 13. Set Hunt harrowing bean ground in Carter's field, George and Lucas sowing manure on wheat sown part of Long Lanes. Moore taking out water furrows in Long Lanes and Carter's fields. Myself and three more hands with three carts are carting mangold over to Rookland all day. The governor complains of a bad head but is in a very good temper.
Weather. Fine, with cold wind, drying the land up beautifully.

Monday November 15. The two carters and George putting in wheat in Old Woods. Lucas water furrowing. In the afternoon Moore ploughs maize ground. I go over to Rookland with the horse and cart and am there for the rest of the day helping to get in mangold. My thoughts today run much on the dear home ones and I feel I would like to be with them.
Weather. Dull and cold wind.

Tuesday November 16. Set Hunt harrowing in wheat in Uptons after Lucas who is sowing. Moore ploughing maize ground in Old Woods. Abbey, Steve and I are over Rookland all the morning carting in mangold which we finish by one o'clock. I have a hard morning's work throwing up in the barn. In the afternoon we cart from Hovel field to the barn.
Weather. Cold wind, little snow in the morning.

Wednesday November 17. Up at the usual time and set the two carters ploughing in Old Woods in the cabbage and mustard pieces. George finishes sowing manure in Old Woods and goes on in Uptons. Lucas and Banfield water furrowing and dirting up mangold pies. Steve breaks the shaft of the bullock van in going after the sheep, so have a little running about in consequence, otherwise I am busy all day harrowing in manure in Old Woods. The sheep are brought back, only reach 37*s*. 0*d*. making the governor not very good tempered, market glutted.

Weather. Bright with cold wind.

Thursday November 18. Woke up in time but went to sleep again, follow the governor to the farm. Hunt goes to the station after a ton each of maize gluten and middlings. Moore ploughing in mustard in Old Woods all day. In the afternoon Hunt harrows in manure in wheat sown part of Uptons. I with four more are busy carting mangold in the Gurze getting together fifty-seven load. Have a bit of a row with the governor before breakfast about position of mangold pie, but it passes off alright.

Weather. Bright with cold wind.

Friday November 19. I cycle to Mr. Stevens with a bill and having some time to spare I cycle as far as Cowfold and back. The two carters are set ploughing mustard and headland in Old Woods. Steve and I are picking up spoiled seed clover in Hovel field and carrying to the mangold pie and one load home. In the afternoon Moore ploughs the remaining corner of the tare ground in the Gurze and George sows wheat on piece of fallow, Hunt following with heavy drags. I am covering up mangold pie with litter in the afternoon. The governor goes to rent audit.

Weather. Very cold wind and clear.

Saturday November 20. Set Hunt and George finishing off sowing wheat in the piece of the Gurze. Moore ploughs the headlands of Old Woods and in the afternoon goes over to Goffland after six sacks of seed wheat. In the morning I cover up the mangolds in Honeypool barn and help mangold cart. Am carting again in the afternoon, finishing off Hovel field.

Weather. Clear cold and bright.

Sunday November 21. In the evening Kathleen and I cycle to Ashington. We get another read sermon.

Monday November 22. Set all hands on lime cart in Long Lanes, putting it on fallow piece. In the morning I take a load of cake over to Rookland, then Cheesemore and I get a load of litter and take two load of mangolds out for the sheep. In the afternoon I go cottoning[1] wheat in the Gurze and Old Woods to keep off the rooks. When coming up to wash I enjoy a couple of slices of Mother's spotted dog, or whatever it is called, call it what you like it is good.

---

1 Stretching cotton over sown ground to keep birds off.

Weather. Still frosty and bright.

Tuesday November 23.   Cows start lying in all day.

Down to the farm and sent Hunt to the station after two ton of cotton cake. Moore and the other hands go mangold cart in the Gurze, taking some to the farm and putting some in Old Barn. In the morning I help drive some heifers over from Rookland and cotton a piece of wheat in Old Woods. In the afternoon I go over to the mill and bring back three bushels of hog corn and seven bushels of ground beans. Ploughing out of the question today owing to frozen soil.

Weather. A very sharp frost and colder.

Wednesday November 24.   Set the men mangold cart from the Gurze to Old Barn. After finishing this they go carting dirt from the mixen[1] into Oxons meadow. I look round at the heifers before breakfast and afterwards get ready for going to market. I go over to Rookland with the milk cart, pick out half a dozen sheep and start off. They only fetch 39s. 6d. today. Get home again about four fifteen. George has a day off to take his pig to market. Am feeling very tired and sleepy tonight. Mangold cart finished at last.

Weather. Dull and very cold.

Thursday November 25.   Up at the usual time and set the men wheat sowing in Long Lanes and Old Woods. The governor goes off to Pulborough directly after breakfast to buy a bull to put with the heifers. In the afternoon I clear up the stores ready for next threshing day. Mother and Father come to tea. I cycle back a little way with them, call in Burgesses coming back and have a comfortable sit round their fire till half past seven. Feel rather upset tonight. Mrs. Venn complains of too much mending. Oh dear what a thing it is to be a lodger.

Weather. Milder, frost giving out.

Friday November 26.   Set Moore and one of the Merrits ploughing in Short Lanes, Hunt harrowing in manure in Old Woods and Long Lanes, George and Lucas sowing manure in both fields. In the morning Banfield and I shoot some beans in the stores and then walk to Dan Hill Crossway after a bull which Mr. Venn bought at Pulborough yesterday. The threshing tackle comes in and in the afternoon we thresh oats from Rushetts and some from Eight Acres getting one hundred and fifty-nine sacks.

Weather. Fine but rather dull.

1   A dung heap.

Saturday November 27.   Down to the farm with the boss, set Moore and one of the Merrits ploughing in Short Lanes. Hunt finishes harrowing in manure in Long Lanes. I am helping with the threshing in the morning, we finish the rick about eleven o'clock. In the afternoon Hunt goes ploughing in Long Lanes and Banfield takes Merrit's place. I am busy cottoning Uptons wheat and mustard piece in Old Woods. The threshers start and finish Tenchford wheat rick getting forty-two sacks.

Weather. A little rain in the evening otherwise fine.

Monday November 29.   Went down to the farm with the boss and set the two carters and George ploughing in beans in Stock Park. Lucas water furrowing. In the morning I saw up a few logs, then Mr. Venn and I go to the farm and put up some wheat and do some bullock driving. The ploughing stops after dinner owing to heavy rain and we go into the barn and winnow some tail oats. I do not like farming on wet days.

Weather. Pouring wet day, very unpleasant after all the fine weather.

Tuesday November 30.   Number of days fine in November – 26; with wet – 4.

Sent Hunt to the station for two ton of coal. George sowing basic slag on Crab Tree Croft with manure drill. In the afternoon, Hunt, Moore and George go ploughing in beans in Stock Park. Mr. Venn and myself go over to Rookland and dress some of the sheep's feet. Go over to Burgesses in the evening for a chat. One more month nearer to the end of my apprenticeship.

Weather. Bright and warm.

Wednesday December 1.   Went down to the farm with the boss and set the two carters and George ploughing in beans in Stock Park, at which they continue all day. After breakfast I get ready to go to Steyning market with half a dozen sheep. I go over to Rookland and get loaded up. Have a terribly wet ride there getting my overcoat wet through, making me feel very miserable. Today they fetch 38s. 6d. and 42s. 0d. Have a fine journey back.

Weather. Very heavy rain first part of the day, fine after.

Thursday December 2.   Set the two carters and George ploughing in beans in Stock Park. The two boys swede pulling and Lucas spreading in the meadows. I get cake and oats ready for the sheep. In the afternoon I take a turnip cutter, cake, oats and a trough over to the Gurze for the remaining eleven fat sheep, which I fetch over from Rookland. The governor is away nearly all day, going over to Mr. Norman's.

Weather. Dull but fine morning, wet afternoon and very rough evening.

Friday December 3. Up at the usual time, set the two carters and George carting cavings into the lower yard. I go to Partridge Green station after a Dutch cow the governor bought yesterday from Mr. Norman. I have a walk round in the afternoon and take some hurdles to Old Barn to make a pen for the sheep. Mr. Venn and his brother are away all day looking at a farm near Brighton.

Weather. Boisterous wind and stormy.

Saturday December 4. A pouring wet morning, set the carters on horse clipping and getting in the cowman's mangolds. George, Lucas, the two boys and myself go winnowing oats in the morning. In the afternoon Moore goes dung cart and Hunt goes to the station after two ton of middlings, George repairs thatch on ricks. In the afternoon I look round and feed the sheep.

Weather. Pouring rain first thing, heavy storms through today.

Monday December 6. Owing to rain yesterday evening I am unable to return to Dial Post till this morning so Amy gets up and prepares breakfast for me and I start away about seven thirty-five getting here in time for breakfast. Hunt finishes slagging[1] Crab Tree Croft and does some of Old Barn plats, Moore slag and mangold cart. I pen the eleven sheep in Old Barn hovel and start doing their feet. In the afternoon the two carters and George go ploughing in Stock Park. The governor and I finish the sheep and I help take out a load of oat straw to Old Salts for the heifers. The household seems in a very good temper today.

Weather. Fine day, rain at night.

Tuesday December 7. Went down to the farm by myself (the governor going early to Smithfield show) and sent Hunt to the station after two ton of cotton cake. Moore and George ploughing in Stock Park. After breakfast Percy and myself go drilling slag in Old Barn Plat. In the afternoon Hunt fetches some straw from Honeypool to Old Salts and then goes ploughing. I see to the stock in the evening. Threshing tackle comes in.

Weather. Dull but fine, rimy.

Wednesday December 8. Set all hands threshing wheat rick from Stock Park getting seventy-four sacks. I see to the sheep and stock before breakfast and afterwards get ready for market. Steve and I drive down three fat cows from Lindfield and the governor follows in the milk cart with five sheep and a calf. Cows sell at £17. 15*s*. 0*d*., £17 and £10. 10*s*. 0*d*.; sheep three at 38*s*. 0*d*., two at 44*s*. 0*d*. I return about four o'clock and see to the feeding again. Threshers finish at half past three.

---

1 Slag is the refuse separated from metal in the process of smelting.

Weather. Bright and clear.

Thursday December 9.   Set the men on getting out the beans from Old Barn
and bringing them to the farm for threshing. After breakfast I help load the
beans. We clear out the barn by about half past twelve and finish threshing
about half past two, getting twenty-three sacks. In the afternoon the men
go carting dirt from the mixen on to Oxons meadow. The boss and I get
the two heifers up to Lindfield for fattening.
    Weather. Rather dull, but fine.

Friday December 10.   Went down to the farm with the boss and set the two
carters and George ploughing in Stock Park, which they finish and then go
to Oxons. One of the cowmen is laid up with a sprained ankle, so in the
morning I help get in their mangolds. In the afternoon I help get the
governor off to Worthing with some rabbits, packing them, etc., and then
turn the heifers from Old Salts into Oxons and feed the sheep. Mr. Venn
gets back about seven o'clock. In the evening I get a lecture on the ways of
men employed on the farm, very edifying of course (Oh yes).
    Weather. A drizzly rain continues all day.

Saturday December 11.   The two carters and George ploughing in Oxons.
In the morning I go caving cart with the boys. In the afternoon I help get in
the cowmen's mangolds and take some cavings out to Crab Tree to cover
up the mangold pie and also pick up the remaining clover seed in same.
Saturday night comes round again with its old welcome. The mud and
mess today has been dreadful, if you want to see any slush come to Dial
Post.
    Weather. Drizzly rain continues nearly all day.

Monday December 13.   The servant failing to return last night I get up and
light the fire. The governor stays in bed all day with pains in his back so I
have the farm to myself. Set the two carters and George ploughing in
Oxons. I look round and feed the stock under my care before breakfast and
afterwards I dress the sheep's feet over at Old Barn and then go to
Rookland and do one or two affected ewes. In the afternoon I take some
straw and hay up for Banfield and cart some hay out to the heifers. Am still
feeling a little out of sorts.
    Weather. Fine, getting colder towards evening.

Tuesday December 14.   Mr. Venn gets up but not out. I set the two carters
and George ploughing in Oxons, Lucas hedge-trimming. In the morning I
drive the cowman with a sprained ankle to the Burrell Arms to see the
doctor whom we just manage to miss, so have to drive all the way to
Cowfold, getting back to dinner about half past two. Being such a short

afternoon I have a tremendous rush to get through my duties, having to rush here, there and everywhere. In the evening I pack forty-three rabbits and eleven fowls for Worthing.

Weather. Bright and clear, cold blow.

Wednesday December 15. Mr. Venn still stays in bed first thing. I set the two carters and George finishing ploughing in Oxons and then going to Tenchford field. I see to the feeding of stock etc., before breakfast and afterwards have to go over to Rookland after a sick pig, which I bring home and it is killed. I also go burning trimmings in Tenchford. In the afternoon Banfield and I get a load of oat straw for Honeypool. The governor does not get to the farm today. I have another very busy time to get round by dark.

Weather. Fine morning, we get a slight fall of snow in the afternoon.

Thursday December 16. The two carters and George ploughing in Tenchford. After breakfast I drive Mrs. Wyatt to the station, then go over to Tenchford and shift some hedge trimmings out of the ploughers' way. In the afternoon I put up some corn and take it to the mill, but soon after I start the trace breaks so have to change harness, hindering me rather, do not get back till nearly dark, making me rather late in finishing. Mr. Venn gets to the farm today.

Weather. Ground snow clad in the morning but soon passed off with rain showers.

Friday December 17. The gov. still lies abed. Set Moore and George ploughing in Tenchford. Hunt goes to the station after two ton of extra oil cake. In the morning I go to Tenchford and finish shifting the hedge trimmings. In the afternoon Hunt joins them at plough. I help the cowmen a little and then give the boys a hand littering up the yard. Everything and everywhere in a terrible mess and slush.

Weather. Dull morning wet afternoon.

Saturday December 18. My watch stops so am a little late this morning. Send the two carters to Washington after two waggon load of chalk. The two Lucases go winnowing wheat all day doing one hundred and eight sacks. I see to feeding the stock before breakfast and afterwards go to the farm and help with the winnowing. In the afternoon I do likewise. Am feeling very well and happy today. Thoughts wandering to next Saturday.

Weather. Much better with a clear bright evening.

Monday December 20. Down to the farm with the boss and set all hands on dung cart from the cow yards on to piece of Uptons for maize. In the morning the governor and myself go hedge mending over at Old Barn, to keep the heifers from entering the Gurze. In the afternoon I go over to the mill at Partridge Green and fetch home the corn and feed the stock again in the evening. Hard frost permits of dung cart.

Weather. A very hard black frost, cold and fine.

Tuesday December 21. Send the two carters to the station with twenty-seven quarters of wheat. The two Lucases go dung spreading in Uptons. The governor goes off by the ten o'clock train to Haywards Heath market to buy some cows but fails in his purpose. In the morning I do a little to covering up the mangold pie in Hovel field with trimmings and help the carters load their wheat for the afternoon journey taking another twenty-seven quarters. Am not very busy in the afternoon. I feel as though I have another cold coming this eve.

Weather. Hard frost and very cold.

Wednesday December 22. Up at the usual time. Set the carters doing odd jobs having had a tremendous rainfall during the night, there is very little doing. Lucases winnowing oats, I feed the heifers and sheep before breakfast and afterwards pack fifty-five rabbits ready to go to Worthing. I get ready and drive down to Worthing, get down there about half past twelve, take them to Whitingtons, put up the pony, then go and meet Sid from the office and we go to his rooms and we have dinner together, then we return to the town, Sid going back to work and I get ready for a start Dial Post-wards, arriving there about half past four, after a pleasant day's outing. Grace and Manna arrive today.

Weather. Stormy, and oh so wet underfoot.

Thursday December 23. Go down to the farm by myself and set the two carters caddling,[1] taking up mud scrapings and caving cart. The two Lucases dung spreading and hedge trimming. In the morning I do a little bullock driving from Honeypool with Banfield. In the afternoon I go to the mill Partridge Green for the bean meal. In the evening I clean up my bike and mend a puncture ready for the anticipated home journey of tomorrow.

Weather. Almost a wet day, so wet and unpleasant getting about.

Friday December 24. Set the carters doing odd jobs, getting in straw, etc. I help Hunt load a load of straw in the morning and do the usual stock feeding. In the afternoon I help Moore a little at Honeypool. Let the carters have their oats after tea. I prepare for a ride homewards for the Xmas holidays, starting just before eight and arriving about a quarter to nine.

Weather. Fine.

---

1 Looking around for odd jobs.

Saturday December 25. I am almost ashamed to say what time I turned out this morning, so we will pass it over. After breakfast I busy myself indoors with lighting the stove and fire doing the pumping, etc., get washed about eleven thirty. Sid gets down by an early train in time for breakfast. Ted, Hilda and Harold also arrive. After a good dinner from the good old roast beef of Old England we sit round the fire and receive our presents, all coming off pretty well. In the evening we play bagatelle and whist and after a most happy and enjoyable day retire to rest at eleven thirty p.m. The three boys occupying one bed.
　　Weather. Mild, fine.

Monday December 27. Almost nine o'clock before we sit down to breakfast. Sid gets up early and goes back to business by the eight fourteen from Horsham. Father driving him in. In the morning Father, Ted, Harold and I go for a walk round Itchingfield church, and go in and see a wedding.
　　Weather. Fair, with some rain.

Tuesday December 28. Get up about half past six this morning and prepare for a journey back to Dial Post starting away about half past seven (but not without some Christmas goodies) after having spent a most enjoyable time with loved ones, having been once more all together. I take some corn to the mill in the morning and in the afternoon do some bullock driving. Loved ones are very much in my mind today.
　　Weather. Brighter and fine.

Wednesday December 29. Back once more to the usual rising time. Set the two carters ploughing on Tenchford which they finish afterwards going to a piece in Uptons for maize. We separate the heifers before breakfast and I do some feeding, afterwards I help load the last six sheep for market and then cotton part of wheat in Long Lanes, which I finish in the afternoon. Mr. Venn goes off to market, sheep sell at 40s. 0d. and 41s. 0d. Am very thankful that the last of these have gone.
　　Weather. Very mild and sunny, quite springlike.

Thursday December 30. Go down to the farm and set the men on dung cart to finish off a piece in Uptons, afterwards ploughing it down. I take over the responsibility of looking after the Lindfield stock today so do the feeding etc. before breakfast. Stock comprises three fatting bullocks, five cows and ten heifers. I go over to Partridge Green mill in the morning but failing to get any meal the governor drives over to Ashington mill in the afternoon. I feed the stock again to finish up with.
　　Weather. Misty and rimy.

Friday December 31. Fourteen days with rain this month; seventeen without.

I start work straight away at Lindfield. The carters finish ploughing piece in Uptons and then go to Pond field. In the morning I go over to Rookland and with Cheesemore put up thirty-four sacks of oats. In the afternoon I put some beans up for the mill and get some straw in at Honeypool. The Venns except Nellie and I go to a party at the Looks and return about a quarter to eleven. Having come to the end of 1909 and looking back, one cannot but feel that it has been filled with a Father's love and tender leading. Praise ye the Lord.

Weather. Fine and mild.

1910

A record of my second year's apprenticeship at Dial Post Farm with varied experiences.

Saturday January 1.   Go down to the farm by myself, the gov. not getting home last night till nearly eleven o'clock, having been to a party so feels tired, of course I have to wait up for him but it doesn't matter about me. Set the two carters and George ploughing in Pond field. I am busy at Lindfield in the morning cleaning out calves, etc. I help get in a load of straw for Honeypool in the afternoon, also some mangold for cowmen and some hay for the house. I ask the gov. for a little extra for Sunday work, but 'tis no go, it seems rather hard.
   Weather. Fair, rain in the evening.

Monday January 3.   Do the Lindfield work before breakfast. The boss sets the two carters ploughing in Pond field, George putting on slag in Old Salts and going ploughing in the afternoon. I help the boys litter cart yard in the morning and in the afternoon do a little land measuring for a mangolder and finish up by doing the Lindfield work. Mr. Venn in rather a bad temper today.
   Weather. Fine and very mild.

Tuesday January 4.   Go down to the farm by myself, Mr. Venn having had a bad night with his wife. Set the two carters ploughing in Pond field, George slag sowing in Ten Acres and Old Barn field. In the afternoon Abbey and I get in a load of straw at Honeypool. In the evening I cycle to Cowfold for the doctor for Mrs. Venn who has a festered thumb and being in much pain. Have a very dark ride.
   Weather. Fairly fine with damp mist.

Wednesday January 5.   Do the work at Lindfield before breakfast. Mr. Venn sets the two carters ploughing in Pond field, Lucas hedge-trimming. Directly after breakfast I get ready for market, go over to Rookland and from there drive down three fat bullocks to Steyning. They sell for £18. 0s.

Swathe turning

0*d.* a piece. Get home again about half past four and with George's help do the evening's work at Lindfield.
Weather. Dull but fine.

Thursday January 6. Mr. Venn sets the two carters to plough in Pond field, George slag sowing. In the morning I am busy at Lindfield, bedding up etc. In the afternoon I am odd jobbing. Still an abundance of mud everywhere.
Weather. Mild and damp.

Friday January 7. The governor and his brother go off by the eight twenty train. I go to the farm and send Hunt to the station for two ton of maize gluten.[1] Moore and George finish ploughing Pond field. Hunt goes raftering[2] in Eight Acres in the afternoon. In the morning I am busy with the Lindfield stock and shifting calves over to Rookland. In the afternoon I walk round and see all the men at their work. Mr. Venn's brother settles on a farm near Eastbourne, after many wanderings.
Weather. Dull and a little colder.

Saturday January 8. Up at the usual time and set the two carters and George raftering in Eight Acres. In the afternoon Moore and George are ploughing in Eight Acres. Hunt goes to the station for two ton of cotton cake. I do the work at Lindfield in the morning and various odd jobs. In the afternoon I help Lucas at Honeypool and do my usual feeding duties. Mr. Venn is very dumpy today.
Weather. Drier and a little colder.

Sunday January 9. Go to Billingshurst in the morning, Mother and Father there, I get to no more meetings today. Am feeling very much down today.

Monday January 10. Up at the usual time, have to go to the farm with a key, then do the Lindfield work before breakfast. The two carters and George go ploughing in Rushetts. I do various odd jobs in the morning and in the afternoon get in a load of straw at Honeypool with Abbey's help and finish up with the usual evening work.
Weather. Much finer and brighter, the sun has shone here today for the first time this year.

Tuesday January 11. The governor sends the two carters to Washington for two waggon load of coarse chalk. The Lucases go hedge trimming. I am with Percy nearly all day taking up hedge trimmings and carrying over to Old Barn yard. Mr. Norman pays us a visit.

---

1 Nitrogenous part of the flour of wheat and other grain.
2 Ploughing (land) leaving a space between the furrows.

Weather. Terribly heavy storms last night make it dreadfully wet and dirty underfoot. Today fairly fine with heavy rain at evening.

Wednesday January 12.   Go over to Lindfield and do the work there before breakfast. The gov. sends the two carters to Tidey's West Grinstead with two waggon load of oats going again in the afternoon with the same quantity. Steve and myself go to Steyning market with four bullocks and six pigs. Have a terrible job with one of the bullocks who would jump the hedge, do not get to the market until half past two. They sell well today at £19, £19. 10s. 0d., £19. 10s. 0d. and £19. 5s. 0d. Get home about half past four and with George's help feed the Lindfield stock. Threshing tackle comes in.
Weather. Fairly fine, snow in the evening, very cold.

Thursday January 13.   The governor sets all hands on threshing the oat rick from Thistly field. I go to Lindfield and do the work there before breakfast. I help on the straw rick in the morning and in the afternoon till nearly three o'clock am on the corn rick, when I come home to see Father who drives over to see Mr. Venn about the £2 extra and my Sunday work. Mr. Venn tells Father he cannot seem to make him understand, he gets his £2 and I no pay, still cheer up William. From oat rick 143 sacks.
Weather. A lovely day, quite hot in the sun.

Friday January 14.   The governor sets the two carters and George ploughing in Rushetts. Lucas hedge trimming. In the morning amongst other things I help Steve take up a load of cavings for the Honeypool beasts. In the afternoon Percy and I get in a load of straw at Honeypool. The gov. and I have a talk over yesterday's problem and then dismiss the subject. In the evening he gives me 10s. extra. The clouds of the past few days have lifted and I am feeling much brighter today. The Lord is good.
Weather. Variable, some rain.

Saturday January 15.   Go to Rookland after Cheesemore for threshing and do the Lindfield work before breakfast. The governor sets all hands threshing wheat rick on staddle, getting eighty-six sacks. In the morning Mr. Venn and I drive over to Southwater in the milk cart after a heifer and calf bought of Mr. Grinstead. In the afternoon we go over to Rookland and pick out thirteen of the poorest ewes for better feeding. I come back and do my usual feeding work.
Weather. Fine morning, damp afternoon and evening.

Monday January 17.   The governor goes down to the farm and sets all hands except Hunt dung cart from the cow-yard to under the oak tree. Hunt goes to the station in the morning for two ton of extra oil cake and in the afternoon for two ton of cotton cake. In the morning I help unload the cake and in the afternoon I take some hay and straw to Dial Post. Spend a pleasant evening indoors playing Quit with the girls.

Weather. Heavy storms with bright intervals.

Tuesday January 18. Do the usual morning's work at Lindfield. Mr. Venn sets all hands on dung cart except Hunt who goes to West Grinstead for two ton of coal. Steve and I take up some hedge trimmings in the morning for the road across Carter's field and in the afternoon we get a load of straw for Honeypool. In the evening Mr. Burgess and I go to a political meeting held by the Liberal candidate, Mr. Outhwaite at the saw mills. He makes a very good speech and it is quite an agreeable change, get home about nine fifteen.

Weather. Rain, little or much nearly all day.

Wednesday January 19. The governor sets all hands on dung cart from the cow-yard. I get ready for market, have breakfast and start off to Steyning about nine fifteen with the last two of Rookland bullocks and a barren cow. Bullocks sell today for £17 and £18. Have Percy to help me today. We get home about four thirty. I go to the farm and let the carters have their oats, George doing my evening work.

Weather. Finer and colder.

Tuesday January 20. All hands except Moore dung cart. They finish clearing out the yard today. Moore goes ploughing in Rushetts. In the morning Mr. Venn, Steve and I cart faggots and hedge trimmings to make up the road across Carter's field getting pretty well mud bespattered. In the afternoon we take out some more faggots, etc. Our new boy starts work at the house today and in the evening I show him how to do the Lindfield work.

Weather. Dry and colder.

Friday January 21. Up at the usual time, go over to Lindfield and with the new boy's help do the work there before breakfast. The two carters ploughing in Rushetts, George slag sowing over at Rookland. I have an easy morning looking round at the men. In the afternoon help Steve litter up the cow-yard. Mr. Venn is away nearly all day going to Shoreham for Mr. Norman's mother's funeral. Sharp frost last night.

Weather. Bright and cold.

Saturday January 22. Give my work over to the new boy this morning and go down to the farm with Mr. Venn. Before breakfast I go over to Rookland after a dung cart. All hands on dung cart today from the stable yard to Eight Acres, owing to hard frost. In the morning I help the cow

men get their mangolds and in the afternoon give the Honeypool heifers their mangolds and cover up mangold pie. Lucas away with a bad back.
Weather. Very sharp and cold wind.

Monday January 24.   Set all hands on making up the road across Carter's field with hedge trimmings. I come back and help with the work at Lindfield. In the morning I help Hunt loading hedge trimmings. In the afternoon Steve and I take some straw to Dial Post and a crib[1] from Lindfield to Old Barn. In the evening I go to a Liberal meeting at the Schools. Eleven heifers taken over to Old Barn.
Weather. Rather wet, with rough wet evening.

Tuesday January 25.   Set the two carters and Percy ploughing and pressing lea in Crab Tree field. In the morning I help Steve swede cart to Lindfield, before breakfast feeding with hay the eleven heifers taken over to Old Barn yesterday. In the afternoon Bert and myself get up a load of litter from the farm to Lindfield and I finish up with the feeding at Old Barn. Manna goes away to start in her new school at Richmond today.
Weather. A bitter wind, fairly bright.

Wednesday January 26.   Up at the usual time, set all hands on hauling dung from the stable yard to Eight Acres, the ground being hard with frost. Part of the morning and afternoon Abbey and I are busy hedge-trimming cart to Old Barn yard. The governor goes to Steyning market. In the evening after supper he is most confidential to me, telling me much about Mr. Norman and his dealings.
Weather. Cold and bright.

Thursday January 27.   Go down to the farm with the boss, it being again hard and frosty set all hands on hauling dung out to Eight Acres. I feed the Honeypool stock before breakfast and in the morning take some oats and cake over to Rookland. In the afternoon I shift a cutter from Honeypool to Old Barn and take over three sheep troughs to Rookland, rather a big afternoon's work, making me rather late for tea. Snow begins to fall this evening with a rough wind.
Weather. Cold and bright, very sharp frost.

Friday January 28.   A dreadfully rough wet night. Set the carters getting in mangold for the cow men. In the morning I help Abbey and George winnowing oats. In the afternoon Hunt goes to Tidey's with a waggon load of oats and Moore and I get a load of oat straw for Honeypool and I finish up with my stock feeding. George wood-cutting and Abbey straw tying in the afternoon. The cold dry weather soon gives place to rain.

1   A barred receptacle for fodder.

Weather. Heavy storms of hail and rain continue all day, floods out.

Saturday January 29.   Set the two carters and Percy ploughing and pressing the lea in Crab Tree field. In the morning I bring some hay and straw to Dial Post and in the afternoon Bert and I take up some litter to Lindfield and load back with bush faggots. I feed the stock at Old Barn morning and afternoon. In the evening we are able to see a comet.[1]
Weather. One snow storm, otherwise fine.

Sunday January 30.   Cycle to the chapel at Partridge Green with Kathleen in the evening. The bed makers have failed to visit my room today.

Monday January 31.   This month 14 days with rain, 17 without.
Go down to the farm with Mr. Venn and set all hands on dung cart in the morning. I act as waggoner, going to the saw-mills with a waggon and two horses for a load of timber. The frost having given out the men go ploughing in Crab Tree in the afternoon. I get up a load of swedes for the stock at Dial Post. George moves to Rookland today, Cheesemore moving out. Have a chat with Burgess in the evening.
Weather. Fine and fairly bright.

Tuesday February 1.   Woke up late and have a bit of a scramble to get down in time. Set the two carters ploughing in Crab Tree field. In the morning I am throwing swedes into the barn, whilst the boys are carting them. One of the horses is taken bad at dinner time, so I go down with a drink directly after dinner, having given it to him I then walk him up and down the road a few times, afterwards going over about the swedes which we finish carting.
Weather. Fine and fairly mild.

Wednesday February 2.   Do not wake up till twenty to seven this morning. Mr. Venn sets the two carters ploughing in Crab Tree. I feed the Old Barn stock before breakfast and in the morning Steve and I get a load of rough bushes and take them over for Old Barn yard. In the afternoon Percy and I take over a load of straw for litter and help the governor and Bert drive a heifer to Lindfield having a pretty good job and tearing my trousers.
Weather. Raining nearly all day and dreadfully dirty.

Thursday February 3.   I seem to be rather sleepy this week, do not wake up until six fifteen. The two carters are ploughing in Crab Tree field. After breakfast I go over to Rookland and bring back part of a waggon load of straw and then go over there again with 12 cwt. of basic slag which George puts on Faggot Stack Meadow in the afternoon. After dinner Steve and I

1   This was Halley's comet.

take another load of bushes over to Old Barn and I feed the stock in the evening.

Weather. Fine and fairly mild.

Friday February 4. Up at the right time this morning, ploughing in Crab Tree field continues. After breakfast the governor and I drive a heifer over to Rookland, afterwards coming home and sawing up some logs. In the afternoon I go to the saw mills with a horse and waggon for some more timber. Lucas returns to work today.

Weather. Colder and fairly bright.

Saturday February 5. The two carters finish ploughing in Crab Tree field by twelve o'clock. In the morning I do a little dung spreading in Eight Acres. In the afternoon the carters plough in Rushetts and Percy and myself take over a load of bushes to Old Barn. Lucas and Abbey dung spreading. I finish up by feeding the stock and giving the carters their oats. Farm progress hindered much by the weather. Am glad it is Saturday night again.

Weather. Damp morning, wet afternoon.

Sunday February 6. Do not go to Billingshurst this morning but cycle straight home arriving just after eleven o'clock. Spend a real happy time with loved ones. Thank the Lord for home.

Monday February 7. Set the two carters and Percy ploughing and pressing in Hovel field (lea). In the morning I help put up some corn for the mill and do a little dung spreading with Lucas. In the afternoon Steve and myself take over a load of straw to Old Barn and I finish up by serving the heifers there.

Weather. Heavy showers and very mild.

Tuesday February 8. Set the two carters and Percy ploughing and pressing in Hovel field. I see to the stock at Old Barn before breakfast and afterwards go over with some oats to Rookland in the milk cart. In the afternoon Steve and I get a load of straw from the farm for Honeypool. The governor is away nearly all day, going to Haywards Heath market with Mr. Look. I visit Burgess in the evening and have a chat over the fire. Mr. Venn is fifty-two today.

Weather. Fine morning, wet afternoon.

Wednesday February 9. The carters and Percy ploughing and pressing lea in Hovel field. In the morning Steve and I start clearing out the thatched cart house, sorting bags, etc. In the afternoon Lucas and I mix and put up, basic slag, super, and bonemeal, a nice dusty job. The governor goes to market in the afternoon and sells his white oats.

Weather. Fine and bright.

Thursday February 10. The carters and Percy ploughing and pressing in Hovel field. I help load some patent manure and feed the Old Barn stock before breakfast. Afterwards I help the cowmen get in their mangolds. In the afternoon Steve and I cart some bush faggots and put in the ruts across Carter's field. I have a very nice letter from Ted this morning, enclosing a Postal Order for 2s. 6d. I am not forgotten by my kind brothers and sisters.
     Weather. Fine till evening, then raining.

Friday February 11. Wake up early, but drop off to sleep again. Set the two carters and Percy ploughing and pressing[1] in Hovel field. I help load some manure and feed the Old Barn stock before breakfast. In the morning I burn up bushes and trimmings round Cottage Meadow, and in the afternoon drive over to Ashington mill after some bean meal. I run across a man on the road who is seeking work and have a nice chat with him, finding him fully trusting in the Lord his Saviour.
     Weather. Fine first off, heavy storms later.

Saturday February 12. Go down to the farm with the boss and set the two carters ploughing in Hovel field, no pressing today. In the morning I go burning bushes at Lindfield and in the afternoon an order comes in for ten sacks of oats and being unprepared the governor and I have to winnow them up. I give the carters their corn and finish up with the feeding at Old Barn.
     Weather. A lovely day, like spring.

Monday February 14. Up at the usual time, send Moore to Rooklands after a waggon load of litter and Hunt to Southwater for a one thousand of bricks. In the morning the governor and I help winnow some oats. In the afternoon the carters finish ploughing lea in Hovel field. I drive over to Partridge Green with some rabbits and to the mill with some beans to be ground. Mr. Venn is in a very good temper today.
     Weather. Almost a wet morning, much finer afternoon.

Tuesday February 15. A tremendous fall of rain during the night renders work on the land impossible, so set the carters caving cart and clearing up mangold trimmings. After breakfast Steve and I cart some more bush faggots for road making. In the afternoon Moore goes to the saw mills after timber and Hunt goes to the station for two ton of maize gluten. Steve and myself get a load of straw for Honeypool. Mr. Venn seems rather out of temper with everybody today.
     Weather. Inclined to be showery, but mostly fine.

1 Flattening out the turned furrow left by the plough.

Self binders at work

Wednesday February 16. Set the two carters ploughing in dung in Eight Acres. I feed the stock at Old Barn before breakfast and in the morning Steve and I go faggot cart for road making. Mr. Venn goes off to market about twelve o'clock with a calf. In the afternoon I go out and have a turn at ploughing and help the boys a bit.

Weather. Fine, rather drying.

Thursday February 17. The carters ploughing in dung in Eight Acres. After breakfast I drive the milk cart over to Partridge Green with some rabbits and bring back the bean meal. In the afternoon Percy and I cart some stakes and binders for Lucas to make a hedge. About half past four I have to rush to Partridge Green for the vet, a cow being partially choked. I bring back the choke pipe and we remove the obstruction.

Weather. Occasional storms, otherwise fine, very windy.

Friday February 18. Owing to heavy rain early this morning set the men clearing out muck from the rick-yard, except Moore who goes to the station for two ton of cotton cake. I cycle back to Partridge Green with the choke pipe after breakfast, then go round collecting hurdles. The two carters plough in Eight Acres in the afternoon and Percy and I take a load of hurdles over to Rookland for the lambing pen. The first lamb (a dead one) arrives this morning. I do the usual day's stock feeding.

Weather. Fine after seven a.m., and very windy.

Saturday February 19. Do not wake up till rather late this morning, so the governor precedes me to the farm. The carters finish ploughing in dung in Eight Acres and in the afternoon start ploughing in beans in Dial Post field at Rookland. I go over to Rookland in the morning and help the boss and George pick out the ewes nearest lambing and bring back the mangold drill. In the afternoon I take over the wheelbarrow and some oats with a horse and cart. See to the Old Barn stock as usual.

Weather. Fine, with a strong drying wind.

Monday February 21. Set Hunt, Lucas and Abbey clearing up in the rick-yard. Moore goes after Johnson's furniture. I help with litter cart in the morning. In the afternoon the two carters go ploughing in spring beans in Dial Post field. Steve and I get a load of straw for Honeypool and I do the usual evening feeding. Mr. Venn very chatty in the evening.

Weather. A little rain, rather dull with cold wind.

Tuesday February 22. I lay calmly on this morning mistaking the time for half past five instead of half past six resulting in a mighty rush to dress. Set the two carters ploughing in beans in Dial Post field, but they have to leave off owing to rain, afterwards going faggot and trimming cart for road

making. I go down after breakfast and find Percy stuck with a load of
mangold and failing to get out with three horses we have to unload and
after wallowing about in mud a foot deep manage to get out the empty cart
with two horses. In the afternoon we go winnowing oats. Space fails me to
describe the various interesting events of today.

Weather. Wet morning, finer afternoon.

Wednesday February 23.   It raining hard we set the carters waggon greasing.
Moore afterwards goes to Steyning with two bullocks. Hunt shackling. I
feed the Old Barn stock before breakfast and in the morning help load the
bullocks, then help Hunt get a load of straw for Old Barn. In the afternoon
George comes for me to go over to Rookland, so I go and help him with a
lambing ewe, the lamb coming out all wrong and necessitates killing the
ewe. Mr. Venn goes off to Steyning market and sells the two bullocks
privately for £14. 10s. 0d. and £15.

Weather. Wet first thing, fine and bright later.

Thursday February 24.   Send Hunt to the station for two ton of Soya bean
cake and Moore for two dozen hurdles and stakes. After breakfast I go over
to Rookland with some lambing medicines, staying and helping George all
morning and in the afternoon I go again and we enlarge the lambing fold.
Hunt takes 33 sacks of oats to Mr. Hoar. Moore goes bush cart. The gov.
goes to a meeting at Billingshurst in the evening returning about eleven
o'clock after which I go over and spend the night with George, tending the
ewes, do not go to bed, one twin arrives.

Weather. Wet first thing, finer after.

Friday February 25.   Come over from Rookland about seven o'clock, call
in and have a mouthful to eat and then go over to Old Barn and do my
feeding, then come back to breakfast. Hunt Lucas and Johnson are dung
cart from Lindfield yard to the mixen outside. Moore carting bushes to Old
Barn and for road making. I cut up two dead ewes for boiling in the
morning. In the afternoon I go over to Rookland and we get some poles in
ready for making a lamb shelter in the field. After supper I go over again for
the night in case help should be needed, it being George's turn to watch.

Weather. Wet first thing, showery later on.

Saturday February 26.   Come over from Rookland in time for eight thirty
breakfast, having sat up till one thirty this morning when George relieves
me and I have a comfortable six and a half hours in bed coming very
welcome. Hunt, Lucas and Johnson are dung cart at Lindfield, Moore is
shackling[1] and fetches two dozen hurdles in the afternoon. I am over at

---

1 Turning ones hand to any job.

Rookland all day helping George put up a lamb shelter in the field and go over again at night to take my turn at watching, no lambs arrive either last night or today.

Weather. Very little rain today, more spring-like.

Sunday February 27. Stay in in the morning for fear of anything being wrong with the ewes and am prevented from going out in the evening by a choking cow needing attention.

Monday February 28. This month there have been twenty days with rain, and eight only without.

Come over from Rookland in time for breakfast, having watched the sheep during the first part of the night, getting one lamb, the ewe needing help so had to call George. I go over again after breakfast and help George and get a load of bush faggots. In the afternoon I go over again and we load a waggon load of hay (seed). Another lamb arrives about five fifteen so do not get home to tea till six fifteen. The two carters go to the station twice for flints. Am off to Rookland again directly after tea, so do not change this evening.

Weather. A pouring wet day.

Tuesday March 1. Come over from Rookland in time for breakfast, having had one lamb only, both of us having to stay up till after one o'clock with the ewe. I go over there again in the morning and help George with the work. We put the first ewes and lambs into the field. In the afternoon we put old rick cloths on the lamb shelter in the field. The two carters go to the station twice with forty-four quarters wheat. Total number of lambs so far nineteen.

Weather. Fine and bright, quite a treat.

Wednesday March 2. Get over from Rookland in time for breakfast, having watched from eleven to four. I go over again afterwards and help George clean out the hovel, and clean some mangolds and he cuts my hair during his dinner hour. The two carters go to the station twice for a truck load of flints. I go to Rookland again after dinner and with Bert get a load of bush faggots. The governor goes to market with one cow and two calves. Threshing tackle comes in. Lambs still nineteen.

Weather. Actually another fine day.

Thursday March 3. I am rather late over from Rookland this morning having a ewe lambing just as I am coming away. All hands are busy threshing the oat rick from Pond field today, getting one hundred and fifty-six sacks. I go down after breakfast and help on the straw rick and again in the afternoon and finish up by giving the Old Barn stock their hay.

George gets two more lambs at dinner time. Hunt and the governor have a bit of a skirmish in the afternoon. Go over to Rookland after supper for the night watch.

Weather. Lovely, drying up a treat.

Friday March 4.   I get up an hour earlier than necessary this morning, my watch having stopped, help George a bit with the feeding then come over for breakfast, after which the governor and I drive over two calves. Hunt goes to the station for two ton of coal. Moore and Johnson ploughing in beans in Dial Post field, but have to leave off about eleven o'clock the ground being too wet, afterwards going to the clover ley piece. Hunt fetches a load of hay from Rookland in the afternoon. I clean up the stores ready for winnowing and feed the Old Barn stock.

Weather. Another beautiful day, mud gradually disappearing.

Saturday March 5.   Come over from Rookland first thing in time for breakfast. Moore and Johnson go over to Rookland ploughing clover ley, Hunt goes to the station after two ton of cake (one of Bibby and one of cakeletts). In the morning the governor and I go down to the farm and help winnow thirty-five sacks of black oats for seed. In the afternoon I go over to Rookland and help George with the feeding etc., and again after supper to take my watch over the flock. Hunt straw cart to Old Barn in the afternoon.

Weather. Fine and bright.

Monday March 7.   Get up at eight o'clock and come over here for breakfast after four hours in bed. I enjoy one of Mother's mince pies and a cup of cocoa about midnight. Moore and Johnson go ley ploughing at Rookland, Hunt goes mangold cart in the morning and joins the ploughers in the afternoon. We go down to the farm after breakfast and winnow some more oats and in the afternoon drive over one batch of ewes and lambs from Rookland as far as Ten Acres, and after tea shift them onto Old Pond.

Weather. Another fine, bright day.

Tuesday March 8.   Get over here at the usual time having had four and a half hours in bed. Mr. Venn goes to the farm and sends Hunt to Steyning with a waggon load of oats (thirty-five sacks) Moore, Johnson, Lucas and Abbey go dung cart on to the mangold ground at Rookland. I go over in the morning and afternoon and help drive between. The governor and I have to go down to the ewes and lambs after tea so it makes another late evening for me. Tonie comes to tea too. I get two lambs in my last night's watch, making thirty-five in all.

Weather. Inclined to be damp.

Wednesday March 9. Go to bed at three a.m. get up at eight o'clock, get over here in time for breakfast, afterwards I go into Ten Acres and start burning up the hedge trimmings, but am obliged to leave off before long owing to rain. Hunt goes to Steyning with another thirty-five sacks of black oats. Moore starts ploughing in more beans but has to give over going cart greasing in the afternoon. I hardly know what to get up to but I spar about till it is time to start feeding the stock. Finish winnowing the black oats.

Weather. Almost a pouring wet day making everything as wet and dirty as ever.

Thursday March 10. Do the usual watch over at Rookland and come over in time for breakfast. The two carters and boys go mangold cart in the morning. The governor and I go down after breakfast and Johnson and myself go putting on patent manure on Oxons (bone and super mixed), he and Lucas having mixed it. In the afternoon Hunt goes to Rookland after a load of hay. It takes nearly all the afternoon to finish sowing the manure. Mr. Venn and I go over to Rookland directly after tea and by the time we return I am feeling rather tired and done up.

Weather. Fine and very close.

Friday March 11. Come over from Rookland in time for breakfast. Mr. Venn goes down to the farm and sets Hunt on rolling Oxons meadow with cylinder roller. Moore goes to Ashhurst with twenty sacks of oats. After breakfast Steve and I go with a horse and cart to fetch home a lambless ewe so as to put another lamb with her. In the afternoon I go over to Rookland and help George shift some ewes and lambs, then get back to the farm and load up oats, cake, etc., for Rookland. I go over rather earlier this evening so as to enable George to go to the school concert.

Weather. Dull, little rain at evening.

Saturday March 12. I journey over from Rookland at the usual time and have breakfast. Mr. Venn goes down to the farm and sets Moore and Johnson rolling meadows (Honeypool, Cottage and Nine Corners). I go over to Rookland again after breakfast and help George clean out the calves and various jobs. I also go again in the afternoon and we drive over another batch of ewes and lambs twenty-three of each and put them in Torry Mead. The governor feels very queer this afternoon so goes home early. I return to Rookland again after supper for the night watch.

Weather. Fairly fine, otherwise rather inclined to drizzle.

Sunday March 13. Cycle to Partridge Green in the evening with Kathleen, returning with Tonie nearly all the way. Sundays go so quickly.

Monday March 14. Sharp frost this morning.

Got up just before eight o'clock and came over here for breakfast, having had a fruitless watch. The gov. goes to the farm and sets the labourers dung spreading on mangold ground and the two carters ploughing in same at Rookland. In the morning Martin and I go faggot cart from Dial Post field home, making a stack of them and in the afternoon Steve and I continue with the same job. Hunt returns having been laid up with the flu since Friday dinner time. Rookland again at night.

Weather. Beautiful.

Tuesday March 15. Come over from Rookland in time for breakfast having had a fruitless watch again. Mr. Venn sets the carters ploughing the mangold ground at Rookland. Bert and I go faggot cart from Short Lanes home. In the afternoon we take a calf up to Lindfield and then go to Old Pond after a lambless ewe and bring it up here for another lamb. Go over to Rookland early this evening, George wanting to get away.

Weather. Bright and fine.

Wednesday March 16. After another fruitless watch I come over in time for breakfast. The gov. sets the two carters ploughing swede and mangold ground in the Gurze. In the morning I go burning bushes in Lashmers but have to go over to Rookland with Mr. Venn about eleven o'clock to attend to a lambing ewe. In the afternoon the boys and I winnow up ten sacks of black oats for Mr. Tidey and I finish up by feeding the ewes and lambs. A young French person comes today for a short stay, being Nellie's friend. Mr. Venn goes to Steyning market after dinner.

Weather. A1. drying up beautifully.

Thursday March 17. Come over from Rookland in time for breakfast, having had a watch without any lambs. Mr. Venn sends Hunt to plough in the Gurze and Moore finishes off putting in the beans in Dial Post field, going to the Gurze after dinner. In the afternoon I go burning hedge trimming rubbish in Lashmers and puncture mending in the evening. Eunice arrives this evening for a holiday.

Weather. Dull first thing but clears up and is nice and bright.

Friday March 18. Get over from Rookland at the usual time for breakfast, having had no more lambs. The governor goes down to the farm and sets Lucas sowing oats in Tenchford field, Hunt following him with heavy drags and Moore harrows it in the afternoon. I walk down and have a look at them sowing, then go burning the hedge trimming rubbish with Percy and the same in the afternoon. Lambing, for me, is finished today. I go to bed here at the usual time feeling very thankful to be able to have a good night's rest again.

Weather. Fine except for very heavy snow storms at intervals.

Saturday March 19.   Lambs now number fifty-three.

Back once more to the old rising time. Set the carters ploughing in the Gurze, finishing there they make a start in Clapper field. I go over to Rookland in the morning, in the afternoon Percy and I move the sheep troughs down to the middle ley and take out the Honeypool mangold. Steve finishes off Tenchford field with another harrowing. Have a pretty good job in the evening driving the ewes and lambs through a muddy gateway, and after unavailing efforts have to drive them another way, arriving home about a quarter to eight o'clock.

Weather. Rather a cold blow but fine.

Monday March 21.   Bull put over to Honeypool today.

Owing to frost set the men mangold cart, later Moore and George are oat sowing at Rookland, putting in the ley and Hunt and Lucas sowing in Crab Tree field. I feed the ewes and lambs and Old Barn stock before breakfast and in the morning Mr. Venn and I bring over some more ewes and lambs from Rookland. I go bush burning in the afternoon, the governor driving into Horsham.

Weather. Misty morning bright afternoon.

Tuesday March 22.   Up at the usual time and set all hands mangold cart first off, afterwards Lucas and Hunt finish sowing Crab Tree field. Moore cross-harrows ley piece at Rookland in the morning, Percy cross-harrowing in Crab Tree. I feed the bullocks and sheep before breakfast, then Mr. Venn and I drive down some ewes and lambs and I burn some more rubbish. In the afternoon I see Moore cross-harrowing in Crab Tree and do some more burning and feed the sheep at Honeypool, and at Old Barn.

Weather. Fine and bright.

Wednesday March 23.   All hands mangold cart first off. Afterwards Hunt and Lucas go putting in white oats in Oxons. Moore goes to the station for two ton of cotton cake. Percy cross-harrowing in Crab Tree, where Moore goes in the afternoon. In the afternoon I attend to one or two crippled lambs and finish up by feeding the sheep and at Old Barn and Honeypool. The governor drives to Steyning market after dinner.

Weather. Fine and bright.

Thursday March 24.   Hunt has a holiday to seek for a place. Go down to the farm with Mr. Venn and send Johnson to the station for two ton of patent manure. Moore drag harrowing in Oxons after Lucas sowing. I feed the ewes and lambs and bullocks before breakfast and in the morning do some more burning. In the afternoon Johnson goes drag harrowing and Moore finishes cross-harrowing in Crab Tree. I feed early and then help Martin get a load of hay. Am feeling very disappointed tonight as I had thought to be in Worthing with Sid, but not a word of holidays do I hear.

Weather. Fine but dull.

Friday March 25.   Set the men finishing off Oxons for half a day. I feed the heifers and sheep before breakfast and after asking Mr. Venn for a holiday get ready and start off for Worthing about ten thirty. Just this side of Worthing I meet Sid and Amy off for a trip to Chanctonbury Ring so I turn back and go with them. After having a most enjoyable time on the hill return to Sid's flat and Amy comes over and we have tea about four thirty. At seven thirty we go to a sacred concert at Christ Church. I enjoy a night's rest with my old mate Sid.

Weather. Lovely.

Saturday March 26.   Hunt leaves.

We get up about seven thirty a.m. and prepare our breakfast consisting of fried bacon. Sid is on duty at nine fifteen, I go with him almost to the office, then have a ride round the West part of the town viewing familiar scenes. I then make tracks for Lucerne arriving just after twelve o'clock, having had a very good run.

Weather. Rather dull but fine.

Monday March 28.   Get up about eight fifteen and after breakfast I help Father give the colt a run round. I then give the bees a spring clean and thorough over-hauling and transfer one lot to a new hive. I have rather a lazy afternoon supplemented with a cup of tea. We have a little singing after tea and then I begin to think of making a start for Dial Post again, after a real happy Eastertide with loved ones.

Weather. Glorious.

Tuesday March 29.   Back once again to the old order of things, send Moore over to Rookland harrowing wheat, George sows super on about two acres. The new carter Gumbrell and his mate go harrowing in Hovel field, one with drags and the other with wooden harrows. I feed the Old Barn heifers and sheep before breakfast and afterwards go back to my old job of rubbish burning. In the afternoon I go over to Rookland to dress the sheep's feet for footrot. Work has gone off very well today.

Weather. Fine, quite hot.

Wednesday March 30.   Go over to Rookland first off after some whipp-ances,[1] the boss sets the two carters and Bletchley ploughing the remaining part of Short Lanes which they finish. I feed the Old Barn sheep and stock

1   Part of harness attaching plough to traces.

before breakfast and afterwards I go down and dress some lambs and ewes for foot-rot until eleven o'clock and then I drive up the milk cart and having had lunch Mr. Venn and I drive to Steyning with two calves, getting back about half past four, after which I have to go down and let the carters have their oats, feed the beasts at Honeypool and Old Barn and then run about after the sheep, they having got out, do not get home to tea until about a quarter to seven. I feel very much tonight how helpful it would be if I had a confidential friend here, I feel very lonely sometimes.

Weather. Fine, colder.

Thursday March 31. Up at the usual time and set Gumbrell rolling out in the Gurze, other hands threshing out clover seed. George being at work on the farm I go over to Rookland and have a look at the ewes, just in time to see one through the lambing. In the afternoon Moore goes lift-harrowing in Uptons, Gumbrell drag harrowing in the Gurze. I finish up with the usual feeding and visit Johnson and Burgess in the evening, have got a bit of a cold hanging about me today, feeling a little home-sick.

Weather. Dry with a bitterly cold wind.

Friday April 1. Get Gumbrell rolling in the Gurze and Moore harrowing in same after Lucas who is sowing white oats. After breakfast I go cleaning mangolds at Old Barn and do some more burning. In the afternoon Mr. Venn and I with Ketchell go drilling oats and tares mixed in Uptons, putting in about an acre. Finish up with the usual evening's feeding. I am feeling rather dull and heavy tonight with a cold.

Weather. April opens with a strong biting North-east wind and very cold.

Saturday April 2. Set Moore and Gumbrell working down the oat sown piece of the Gurze. Ketchell takes a waggon to Rookland and finishes harrowing the wheat there. I go to Rookland after breakfast and George and I load the waggon up with hurdles and Ketchell and I bring them over to the Gurze. In the afternoon Moore harrows in Short Lanes. I help unload the hurdles and see to the stock. My cold is rather better today.

Weather. Fine and milder.

Monday April 4. Set the men to work in Short Lanes, Lucas sowing oats, Moore harrowing, Gumbrell drag harrowing. I feed the Old Barn heifers and see to the ewes and lambs before breakfast. In the morning I go to the Gurze and pitch a fold on the turnip greens ready for the sheep. In the evening Mr. Venn and I go to the farm and tail forty-six lambs.

Weather. Fine, a nice gentle rain commences in the evening, being just what is needed.

Tuesday April 5.   Up at the usual time and set the three carters ploughing in Clapper field, Lucas hedging. I drive the sheep down to the Gurze before breakfast. In the morning I sharpen some stakes and start pitching a fold when Mr. Venn comes for me to go over to Rookland with him after some ewes and lambs. In the afternoon Steve and I go rolling after the ploughs in clapper field with the big mare and napper[1], a leg aching job, the ground being very rough.

Weather. Fine with cool breeze.

Wednesday April 6.   I get up rather earlier this morning so as to get my work done in time to go to market. The three carters are ploughing in Clapper field in the morning, in the afternoon they go rolling in Ten Acres and Burchells. Steve and I start off to Steyning about a quarter to ten with two fat cows, they travel very well today. It rains fast nearly all the way there, but we have a fine return journey, after which I go round and do my feeding. Cows together fetch £33. 5s. 0d.

Weather. A nice steady rain all the morning, fine with a cold wind in the afternoon, rain again in the evening.

Thursday April 7.   Go down to the farm with the boss and set the two carters rolling, finishing Ten Acres, Torrey Mead and Burchells. Ketchell chain harrows Torrey Mead. In the afternoon all three are ploughing in Clapper field. I feed the Old Barn heifers and get back to an early breakfast, Eunice going off by the 9 train. In the morning I pitch a fold for the sheep on the turnip greens and clean some mangold at Old Barn. In the afternoon Lucas and myself winnow and prepare the clover seed for sale.

Weather. Dull, rather inclined to be wet.

Friday April 8.   Go down to the farm with Mr. Venn and set the three carters ploughing in Crab Tree field, which they finish by dinne time and in the afternoon make a start on Hovel field. I pitch a fold in the Gurze after breakfast, then walk round to see them ploughing. In the afternoon I set another fold, drive down some more sheep and do some foot-rotting. The gov. goes off to the horse sale at Steyning in the morning. Johnson rolling seeds in Lashmers in the afternoon.

Weather. A nice growing day, sunny and warm.

Saturday April 9.   Set the men sowing white oats in Clapper field, getting it all in by leaving off time. I give the ewes their corn and feed the heifers with mangolds and hay before breakfast and afterwards go down and carry the hurdles and pitch a fold, in the afternoon I prepare another fold for Sunday. Gumbrell harrows rolled part of Short Lanes in the afternoon.

1   A horse that nods off while working.

Weather. The same as yesterday.

Sunday April 10. Cannot go to Partridge Green in the evening owing to a punctured tyre – am rather disappointed.

Monday April 11. Go down to the farm and set Gumbrell and Ketchell ploughing in Hovel field. In the morning the governor and I go down and sack up some oats and sharpen some sheep shears. In the afternoon Johnson goes rolling in Clapper field. I go to the Gurze and pitch a fold and finish up with the usual feeding. I go visiting at Burgesses, Johnsons and Weavers in the evening.
Weather. Fine and rather hot.

Tuesday April 12. Mr. Venn away nearly all day at Haywards Heath market to which we send four cows. Up a little earlier this morning, going round to see that Abbey has done his early feeding right. Set Gumbrell and Ketchell finishing off Clapper field and afterwards going to plough in Hovel field. Moore goes to the station for two ton of maize gluten and in the afternoon is at plough. I feed at Honeypool, Old Barn and the sheep before breakfast and set a fold in the morning. In the afternoon I go to Rookland and dress the ewes feet. I go puncture mending in the evening and find that a nasty trick has been played on me by puncturing my back tyre and I find no less than five holes in one place.
Weather. Showery.

Wednesday April 13. The three carters ploughing in Hovel field. Mr. Venn goes off to Steyning market in the morning with a calf. In the afternoon, with Steve's help, I help trim up some of the ewes and we make another fold. Johnson goes rolling seeds in Lashmers in the afternoon finishing the field. In the evening I have another go at my bike finding two more holes and take it all to pieces.
Weather. Very heavy storms with bright intervals, thundery.

Thursday April 14. Up at the usual time, set the three carters ploughing in Hovel field. I do the usual feeding before breakfast and in the morning go over to the Gurze and pitch two folds. In the afternoon I carry out a lamb trough and start giving the lambs some cake and clean some mangold at Old Barn and then finish up with the usual feeding. I am at my bike again in the evening, finish puncture, or rather pin-prick-mending at last and get a new tyre.
Weather. Fine, dull and very mild.

'Dressing the sheep's feet for foot-rot'

Friday April 15.   Down to the farm with the boss and set the men sowing
black oats in Hovel field. I see to the feeding of the heifers and ewes and
lambs before breakfast and in the morning go down and pitch two folds,
making a rather hard morning's work. The men have to stop work in
Hovel field about three o'clock it coming on to rain heavily, just enough to
make it messy and then it leaves off. We go into the stores afterwards and
sort out sacks and do some winnowing. Have a high tea in honour of Mrs.
Venn's birthday.
    Weather. Fine except for one heavy shower.

Saturday April 16. Gumbrell drag harrowing in Eight Acres, Ketchell chain-harrowing meadows. Moore goes to the station for two ton of cotton cake. I set a fold for Sunday and in the evening get my bike in running order ready for tomorrow and start enamelling it.
Weather. Very showery.

Sunday April 17. I cycle home with the butter and cream and spend a few pleasant hours with loved ones.

Monday April 18. Up at the usual time and set Moore harrowing sown piece of Hovel field and Gumbrell drag harrowing other piece for mangolds. Ketchell mangold cart. I feed the heifers and sheep before breakfast and afterwards go down and pitch a fold with Steve's help. In the afternoon the carters go ploughing unsown part of Carter's field. I go over to Old Barn mangold cleaning. Mr. Norman comes and we tail the remainder of the lambs and castrate them.
Weather. Fine drizzly rain all day, miserable.

Tuesday April 19. Send the two carters to the station one for seventeen quarters of oats and one for coal. I am busy all morning carrying and pitching hurdles. In the afternoon Gumbrell goes to Rookland with straw and Moore ploughs in Carter's field. I help Johnson load two load of oats and bring up here, and see to the sheep to finish up. In the evening I cycle to Partridge Green for a hair cut. Manna arrives for her holiday.
Weather. Dull and mild.

Wednesday April 20. The three carters go over to Rookland putting in Manitoba wheat, next to the mangold ground, drilling it in. I feed the heifers with mangold and hay and give the sheep their corn before breakfast. In the morning I help Johnson load some cord wood, then go to the Gurze and pitch two folds. In the afternoon the gov. and myself go to Short Lanes and set Johnson on harrowing with Parmiter harrow to destroy the kilk, then walk round and view the various crops, oats are coming up on all hands very well.
Weather. Rather dull and very mild.

Thursday April 21. Down to the farm with Mr. Venn and set the men on working down the piece of Carter's field, dragging, rolling, then sowing it with Manitoba wheat then dragging, rolling and harrowing it to finish off. In the morning I pitch nearly three folds. In the afternoon I go burning bushes at Old Barn and see to the sheep last thing. I am feeling very happy today. My room is looking very nice after its spring clean. I am bike enamelling in the evening.
Weather. Fairly dull and wonderfully mild.

Friday April 22.   Up at the usual time and set the two carters harrowing wheat in Long Lanes. Lucas sowing Manitoba in thin places. Moore ploughs shallow, a piece of Carter's field and harrows wheat in the afternoon. I cycle over to Pearses, Wiston after breakfast with some clover seed sieves. Mr. Venn goes to Bournemouth about twelve o'clock until Monday, leaving me in charge. I feel the responsibility rather but 'He is able and He will'. I look round at the work and pitch two folds in the afternoon.
    Weather. Thundery, very hot at times.

Saturday April 23.   Go down to the farm by myself and set Gumbrell harrowing in Long Lanes and then in Carter's field. Ketchell harrows in Old Woods before Lucas who is sowing clover seed. Moore ploughs up mangold pie places in Crab Tree field, then harrows behind Lucas. I am busy all day attending to the work and sheep and have a good deal of running about. I am pay-master in the evening. All well so far. Cows turned out for the first time today.
    Weather. Stormy.

Sunday April 24.   I drive Kathleen and Manna to Billingshurst in the morning.

Monday April 25.   I set the men to work. Gumbrell harrows rye piece in Old Woods twice and then we put in the two mangold pie patches in Crab Tree. Moore cross harrows Old Woods all over making the fourth harrowing to get enough grit to cover the seed. Ketchell harrowing wheat in Carters field. Sid cycles over arriving about a quarter to ten and we go over the farm together and have a pleasant time. I am running about nearly all day attending to the work and sheep. The governor returns this evening.
    Weather. Thundery with cold showers.

Tuesday April 26.   Down to the farm with Mr. Venn and set Gumbrell working down in mangold ground in Hovel field with harrows and roller. Moore and Ketchell ploughing folded piece of the Gurze. I shift the hurdles out of the carter's way before breakfast and feed the sheep and heifers. In the morning I cart out some sheeps' food and make pens to cake the lambs in. We have a horse give out in the afternoon, so have to run round and see everything in working order, the gov. going to Haywards Heath market. I am highly elated by receiving a bonus of 10s. 0d. in the eve which is very encouraging.
    Weather. Cold wind, stormy.

Wednesday Arpil 27.   Set the men on working down piece of ground for mangolds in Hovel field, rolling dragging and harrowing it. In the morning I take some sacks over to Rookland for putting up some oats. I go over in the afternoon and George and I put up thirty-one sacks for Mr. Hoare. Mr. Venn goes to Steyning market about twelve o'clock.

Weather. Fine.

Thursday April 28. Set the men to work in the Gurze working down the folded piece for oats which Lucas sows in the morning. Moore goes to Mr. Hoare's with the thirty sacks of oats. I feed the sheep and heifers before breakfast. For the rest of the day I am busy with the lambs trimming and dressing all their feet. Am feeling very tired tonight and am glad to get to bed.

Weather. Fine except for very cold rain in the evening.

Friday April 29. Go down to the farm with the boss and set Moore and Ketchell harrowing in the Gurze before and after Lucas who is seeding the field. Gumbrell rolling Torrey Mead and in the afternoon in Hovel field. After breakfast I stop up mouse holes under the granary and start clearing up the stores which I finish after dinner. Moore goes to the station after some dried grains for the cows.

Weather. Fine, with rather a cold wind, few showers.

Saturday April 30. Up at the usual time and set the men to work in Hovel field. Moore and Ketchell rolling and harrowing before and after the drill, Gumbrell's horses in the drill, and we start mangold sowing by putting in about five acres. I feed the sheep and heifers before breakfast and in the morning make two scarecrows to put in Long Lanes to keep off the rooks. In the afternoon I look round at the men drilling and shift some faggots in Ten Acres. Here endeth the sixteenth month of my apprenticeship at Dial Post.

Weather. Fine with cold blow.

Monday May 2. Gumbrell starts rolling in the Gurze but rain prevents so he continues on the pastures. Moore and Ketchell ploughing in Dial Post field. After breakfast the gov. and I drive over twenty bullocks to Rookland. In the afternoon I start off from Rookland with ten heifers and drive them to the other side of Bolney, ready to continue their journey to Haywards Heath market tomorrow. I drive them myself from the convent and have the dog.

Weather. Almost a wet day, rather unpleasant.

Tuesday May 3. Set Moore cultivating in Eight Acres, Ketchell chain harrowing, shifting sheep, tackle, etc. Gumbrell rolling pastures. I see to the sheep before breakfast and drive them up to Lindfield, have breakfast and then get ready for market. I cycle to Bolney and then drive the bullocks from there to Haywards Heath market but it is a very poor market and only two of them sell, so have to drive the others part of the way back again, get home about half past seven feeling rather tired.

Weather. Lovely.

Wednesday May 4.   Up at the usual time and set Moore drag harrowing and Gumbrell rolling in Eight Acres. Ketchell harrowing wheat at Rookland. I see to the sheep and make lamb pens before breakfast and afterwards go weeding with Steve in Carter's field. In the afternoon Gumbrell goes rolling in the Gurze and I continue weeding. The steam cultivating tackle comes in this evening ready for action tomorrow. Bert and Chips arrive about nine and I am measured for a suit for Sundays.

Weather. Stormy, bright intervals.

Thursday May 5.   Go down to the farm with Mr. Venn and set Gumbrell rolling over at Rookland. Ketchell cultivating mangold ground also over there and Moore waits on the steam tackle for water, etc. After breakfast I go round and have a look at the steam tackle working and do some more weeding in Carters field and continue through the afternoon. Tackle at a standstill during the afternoon having had a wet morning. Moore fetches manger from Floodgates.

Weather. Wet morning, finer afternoon, very cold.

Friday May 6.   King Edward passes peacefully away at Buckingham Palace at eleven forty-five p.m. Set the men to work. Moore waiting on the steam tackle all day. Gumbrell rolling first in twelve acres at Rookland and then on the mangold ground. Ketchell cultivating mangold ground with lift harrow. After breakfast I go over to Rookland and arrange for working down the ground, then I do a little weeding with Steve in Uptons. Dress some of the ewes' feet for foot-rot and do some more weeding in the afternoon and see the steam tackle at work.

Weather. Cold wind, fairly fine.

Saturday May 7.   Up at the usual time, send Gumbrell to the station for two ton of cotton cake, Moore waiting on the steam tackle, Ketchell rolling after steam cultivator which is at work in Eight Acres. I feed the sheep before breakfast and in the morning go weeding in Uptons' wheat. In the afternoon Gumbrell goes to the station again for two ton of steam coal. I have a look round at the steam cultivating, do some more weeding and feed the ewes and lambs to finish up another week.

Weather. Very cold, snow showers.

Monday May 9.   We get a very sharp frost this morning.

Down to the farm with Mr. Venn, set Moore attending to the steam tackle, Ketchell harrowing and rolling mangold ground at Rookland,

Gumbrell goes to the station twice for two ton of nitrate of soda and two ton of salt. I go over to Rookland after breakfast and George and I dress three calves for ringworm. In the afternoon I do a little weeding.

Weather. Storms with very cold wind.

Tuesday May 10. Spent attending the funeral of Mrs. Jim Terry of Pigeon Hill.

Weather. Lovely, warmer.

Wednesday May 11. Feeling rather stiff and tired after yesterday's ride. Set Gumbrell rolling oats in Tenchford field, Ketchell harrowing in Eight Acres, Moore attending to steam tackle in the morning. The governor goes off to market and in the afternoon I start them drilling mangold in part of Eight Acres (five acres) Gumbrell drilling, Steve harrowing, Moore and Ketchell rolling. I am busy superintending all the afternoon. The steam tackle finish up and depart today.

Weather. Cold wind, fairly bright.

Thursday May 12. Set Gumbrell and Ketchell working down mangold ground at Rookland and Moore goes to the station for two ton of mangold manure. I feed the ewes and lambs before breakfast and afterwards Johnson and I go faggot cart. In the afternoon Mr. Venn, his brother and myself drive over to Mr. Lewis's at Bolney and I drive home six of the eight heifers left there. I get back about eight fifteen feeling very tired.

Weather. Fine except for stormy evening.

Friday May 13. Up at the usual time and set the men to work. Moore and Gumbrell going over to Rookland after two waggon load (one hundred and twenty) of faggots. Ketchell goes rolling pastures at Rookland. I feed the ewes and lambs before breakfast and afterwards go weeding and bush burning. In the afternoon the carters fetch two more load of wood and Ketchell goes rolling in the home field and Nine Corners. I do some more burning and clearing up.

Weather. Almost a wet morning, finer afternoon and evening.

Saturday May 14. The two carters go to Rookland for two waggon load of faggots. Ketchell goes rolling in Nine Corners. After breakfast I go clearing up the faggots with Steve. In the afternoon Moore and Ketchell go to Rookland and we put in two acres of mangold. I lead the front horse of the drill. The milk cart has an accident in the evening, a motor running into it, and breaking both shafts. Mr. Venn does not come in till late so I pay the men on my own hook which turns out alright. Another birthday gone.

Weather. Much milder, quite hot.

Monday May 16.   Bank Holiday.

I get up at five thirty this morning, mend a puncture and see to the sheep and then come back and get ready for a run to Lucerne arriving there about eight fifteen just in time for breakfast. Have a stroll round afterwards and look through the hives. Have dinner and spend most of the afternoon lazing on the lawn. Sid returns to Worthing on his bike about three thirty. Have an early tea and games of croquet and tennis. I return to Dial Post about half past eight.
     Weather. A1.

Tuesday May 17.   Back once again to the old order of things. Gumbrell harrowing, Johnson and Moore rolling in Oxons for mangold, Ketchell rolling wheat in Long Lanes. After breakfast I go clearing up bushes round the hedges. Mr. and Mrs. Venn drive over to Lucerne in the afternoon. I go to Mr. Stevens with a bill and from there to Westlands and I stay there to supper.

Wednesday May 18.   Set Gumbrell cultivating, rolling and harrowing piece for maize in Uptons. Moore and Ketchell working ground in Oxons. I see to the sheep before breakfast and have a walk round to look at the crops afterwards. I help Steve take a load of hurdles to the trefolium, then get ready for market and go over to Rookland and load up with five fat ewes and drive them into Steyning, four fetch £2. 7s. 0d. and one £2. 6s. 6d. Mrs. Venn goes away to Bournemouth today. Johnson and Lucas sowing artificial manure in Oxons.
     Weather. A little rain in the morn, afterwards fine and hot.

Thursday May 19.   Set the men clearing up the various heaps of dung and in the rick-yard, a heavy thunder storm last night renders the ground unworkable. After breakfast I help Mr. Venn put in some lettuce plants and help Ketchell take some hay to Honeypool. In the afternoon Moore and Ketchell go harrowing and rolling in Eight Acres, Gumbrell rolling in Rushetts. I am busy all the afternoon trimming up the sheep with Steve's help.
     Weather. Very close, fine.

Friday May 20.   Moore harrowing and Gumbrell drag-harrowing for mangold in Oxons. Ketchell rolling in Eight Acres. I see to the sheep before breakfast and afterwards go weeding in Old Woods. We all have half-holiday today owing to the funeral of our late King Edward VII. I get washed and cycle home arriving about three o'clock.
     Weather. Bright and hot.

Saturday May 21.   Set the men to work rolling, harrowing and cultivating for mangold in Oxons. Ketchell rolling in Eight Acres. In the morning I am busy couching with the gov. in Oxons. We start drilling mangold about ten o'clock and finish the piece off about four o'clock (seven acres). I am couching again in the afternoon and give the carters their oats and feed the sheep.

Weather. Hot and thundery.

Sunday May 22. Cycle to Ashington (Mission Hall) with Kathleen in the evening.

Monday May 23. Up at the usual time and set the men to work. Moore rolling oats in Crab Tree field, Ketchell doing same at Rookland and in Hovel field, and five carts are on dung cart from the cow-yard to Eight Acres for mangold. I see to the sheep before breakfast. In the morning the governor and I are busy shifting stock at Rookland and in the afternoon I am driving between with the carts. Bert comes over again in the evening about my suit.

Weather. Fine and very hot.

Tuesday May 24. Set the men on dung cart and Moore and Ketchell rolling oats. I get ready for the sheep washing before breakfast and then we wash them. In the morning I pitch the first two folds on the trefolium for the ewes and lambs. I have the same job in the afternoon and also fetch some hurdles and troughs from Lindfield. Very hard work pitching, ground hard and dry.

Weather. Hot with colder wind.

Wednesday May 25. Up at the usual hour and set Gumbell and Moore to finish ploughing in Dial Post field, in the morning Ketchell ploughs for maize in Uptons. I feed the sheep with trefolium before breakfast and afterwards pitch a fold and feed them at dinner time. In the afternoon Moore and Gumbrell are ploughing in dung in Eight Acres. I fetch some hurdles and troughs from Lindfield and make another fold and feed the sheep with trefolium again at tea time, finish up at seven o'clock. Have had a real hard day's work today.

Weather. Colder wind and fine.

Thursday May 26. Gumbrell and Moore are ploughing in dung in Eight Acres, Ketchell working down ground for maize in Uptons. I cut the sheep's food and feed them before breakfast and afterwards pitch two folds and feed them again at twelve o'clock. In the afternoon I attend to the lambs' feed and cut and feed again for the evening meal. Cycle to Partridge Green in the evening for a hair cut.

Weather. Rather cold first thing, but very hot later in the day.

Friday May 27. Go down to the farm with Mr. Venn and set Gumbrell and Moore to finish ploughing in Eight Acres, and start working it down.

Ketchell rolls the mangold drilled piece of Oxons and then chain harrows it to destroy the charlock. I am busy all day seeing to the requirements of my flock and have a fairly easy time today. I purchase a pair of boots from Burgess in the evening for 10s. 6d.

Weather. Not so bright, but rather hot.

Saturday May 28. Set the men to work. Moore goes ploughing in maize in Uptons, Steve rolling and harrowing after him, Ketchell and Gumbrell working ground in Eight Acres. I feed the sheep with trefolium[1] before breakfast, afterwards pitching a fold and feed again at tea time and also make another fold in the afternoon. Do not feel up to much this evening. Mrs. Venn returns from Bournemouth.

Weather. Fine and very hot.

Monday May 30. Set the men on working down the remainder of Oxons field. I do my usual duties with the sheep, feeding and pitching two folds, and attending to some of their feet. I help Kathleen move her chicks into the field in the evening. I receive my new suit from Bert today.

Tuesday May 31. Up at the usual time, set Gumbrell working down ground for swedes in Oxons. Moore's horses go in the drill and they finish up the mangold drilling by putting in the last three acres of Eight Acres. I see to the sheep before breakfast and pitch a fold and feed again at dinner time. I make another fold in the afternoon and feed again at tea time. Shepherding is very unpleasant today it being rather wet and very windy, but the rain does a lot of good.

Wednesday June 1. Down to the farm with the boss and set Moore and Ketchell rolling down mangold ground in the morning. Gumbrell goes to the station for two ton of super phosphates. In the afternoon they go working down ground for swedes in Oxons. The shearers arrive after breakfast so have to get ready and put the sheep into Honeypool barn. I am busy catching the sheep and tying the wool. Mr. Venn goes to market with three fat ewes and a heifer. The ewes fetch £2. 4s. 6d. the heifer £11.

Weather. Fine.

Thursday June 2. Set the men on working down the swede ground in Oxons. I attend to the sheep, feeding and pitching and carrying hurdles for a fold. In the afternoon Mr. Venn drives me over to Lovells farm and I drive back two heifers and a cow getting home about a quarter to eight feeling rather weary.

Weather. Except for rain first thing, fine.

1 Clover.

Friday June 3. Set the men working down the remainder of Dial Post field in the morning. I see to the sheep, feed them, pitch a fold and feed again at mid-day. In the afternoon the carters go harrowing and rolling part of Rushetts for maize and Ketchell chain harrows swede ground in Oxons. I am at work with the sheep again in the afternoon. In the evening I give Nellie her first lesson in bike riding.

Weather. Lovely and very hot.

Saturday June 4. Horses turned out to grass by night.

Up at the usual time and set Moore and Gumbrell working down ground in Rushetts. Ketchell chain harrowing swede ground in Oxons. In the morning I see to the sheep, feeding and pitching a fold and help the cowmen cut their green meat. In the afternoon the carters start ploughing the swede ground. I pitch another fold and finish up with feeding. Saturday night comes with its old welcome. Give Nellie another bike lesson in the evening.

Weather. Fine and very hot.

Monday June 6. Am kept awake a long time during the night by a terrific thunderstorm, the thunder and lightning continuing unceasingly, being the worst I have ever experienced, it is still going on when we get up and pouring with rain. Go down to the farm and set the men oiling their harness and when the rain ceases they go dung cart. Lucas and Johnson are spar making. I go over to Rookland with some stakes in the morning and pitch a fold in the afternoon. Have to turn the sheep out to grass.

Weather. Thundery and in the afternoon very hot.

Tuesday June 7. Moore and Ketchell ploughing up the headland in Dial Post field in the morning. Gumbrell goes harrowing all day in Pond field. I cut for and feed the sheep before breakfast and afterwards make a fold. In the afternoon Moore and Ketchell plough trefolium ground in Uptons, behind the sheep. I pitch another fold and give the evening feed the cutting of which makes the gravy run off in streams.

Weather. Wonderfully close, not a breath of wind all day.

Wednesday June 8. Set the men to work. Moore and Ketchell finish ploughing piece of the trefolium ground and then go drilling and harrowing in tares in Dial Post field. In the afternoon I cotton the maize in Uptons and attend to the sheep. Mr. Venn goes to market.

Weather. Fine and very hot.

Thursday June 9. I am a little bit behind this morning, go down to the farm and set Moore and Ketchell ploughing for swedes in Stock Park. Gumbrell goes to the station for one ton of salt and one of Kainite.[1] I feed the sheep

---

1 Fertilizer.

before breakfast and attend to them for the rest of the day. Gumbrell fetches two ton of nitrate of soda in the afternoon. Seven other hands hard at mangold hoeing finishing Hovel field and starting Eight Acres. I go to Ashington with Nellie in the evening cycling.

Weather. Still very hot, thunder about.

Friday June 10.   We have another heavy thunderstorm just after ten last night and it is raining fast in the morning. Send the two carters to the brickyard for three thousand roofing tiles for Old Barn. In the afternoon the men are carting dung from the yard to the mixen at Lindfield. I attend to the sheep. Cannot touch the mangolds today.

Weather. Dull and very heavy looking, rather weird, very oppressive.

Saturday June 11.   Go down to the farm with the boss and set all hands, carters included, on pulling kilk in the mangold in Eight Acres, it being too wet to hoe. In the afternoon Moore fetched Goatcher's furniture. I get forward as much as possible with the shepherding for Sunday. Mrs. Venn presents me with a pair of gloves in the evening for teaching Nellie to cycle. My proper suit arrives at last.

Weather. Very dull and heavy.

Sunday June 12.   Drive to Billingshurst in the morning with Mr. and Mrs. Venn and Kathleen. Mother and Father out with their new cob.

Monday June 13.   Moore and Ketchell go carting out dung at Lindfield. Gumbrell goes to Rookland for the mower and then works down the ploughed trefolium ground in Uptons for maize. Moore and Ketchell go ploughing swede ground in Oxons in the afternoon. I attend to the sheep feeding, pitching, cutting fodder, etc., and in the afternoon do some horse hoeing in Eight Acres. The maize is drilled in the afternoon and rolled in.

Weather. Much cooler and fine.

Tuesday June 14.   Up at the usual time and set Moore and Ketchell working down swede ground in Oxons. Gumbrell starts mowing seeds in Lashmers cutting about four acres. I attend to the sheep through the day. Do a bit of horse hoeing in Hovel field after dinner till Mr. Venn comes. After tea I have a cycle run to Lucerne arriving about ten to seven and start on the return journey about a quarter to nine.

Weather. Cooler and bright.

Wednesday June 15.   Being rather tired I manage to overlay a bit this morning. Set the men on dung cart on to the swede ground in Oxons taking it from the cow-yard. After attending to the sheep I help drive between with the carts. I help with the manure cart again after dinner until it

is time to attend to the sheep again. The governor goes to Steyning market with a calf. Hoers at work in Eight Acres.
Weather. Fine and fairly bright.

Thursday June 16. Down to the farm with Mr. Venn. Set the men to work finishing dung cart on to Oxons and then the carters go ploughing it in. I attend to the sheep's wants before breakfast and afterwards pitch a fold and dress some of the lambs for foot-rot. Sid cycles over from Worthing in the evening arriving about six thirty and we have a run round the farm together.
Weather. Fine, breezy.

Friday June 17. Up at the usual time and set Moore and Ketchell ploughing in dung in Stock Park for swedes. Gumbrell goes over to Rookland and cuts the field of seeds. I see to the sheep before breakfast and carry hurdles and pitch a fold in the morning. Mr. Venn goes to Brighton for the day. In the afternoon I set Steve on swath turning in Lashmers and feed the sheep again last thing.
Weather. Hot.

Saturday June 18. Go down to the farm with the boss and set Moore and Ketchell working down swede ground in Stock Park in the morning. Gumbrell finishes cutting the last six acres of seeds in Lashmers. I see to the sheep, carry hurdles and pitch a fold. Have a fairly slack afternoon. The governor goes drilling swedes in Stock Park and we finish it after tea. I go down and lead the front horse in the evening.
Weather. Bright and very hot.

Monday June 20. Get up after a sleepless night, having been almost frantic with toothache all night long. Go down to the farm with the boss and send Moore to the station for ten quarters oats, Ketchell takes two waggon load of tiles to Old Barn. Gumbrell goes cutting seeds in Thistly field. We carry about four acres of hay in Lashmers today getting seven load in excellent condition. I attend to the sheep and am on the rick part of the afternoon. Am miserable all day with toothache, but it passes off in the evening which is a great relief.
Weather. Bright and hot.

Tuesday June 21. Up at the usual time having had a good night's rest. Set Gumbrell mowing seeds in Thistly field which he finishes by twelve o'clock. Moore and Ketchell go to Rookland with waggons and start carrying the seed hay. I dress several lambs for foot-rot before breakfast and in the morning am running about with horse and side delivery rakes between the two farms. In the afternoon I am helping on the rick. We clear the seed hay field with eight load. Gumbrell goes rolling in the afternoon.

Weather. Fine and fairly bright.

Wednesday June 22.   Set the carters ploughing in Rushetts. In the afternoon we start carrying the hay in Lashmers. I go working the side delivery rake and after tea am busy loading, get home about a quarter to eight having carried eleven load since dinner.
Weather. Fine and fairly bright.

Thursday June 23.   Turn out at the usual hour. Go down to the farm with the boss and on arriving find that one of the horses has fallen into the brook so have to set about pulling him out, using two horses to do so. Afterwards Moore and Ketchell go ploughing for turnips in Rushetts, rolling it in the afternoon. Gumbrell mows the grass in Crab Tree Croft. In the morning the gov. and I recotton the last sown maize, and I pitch the first fold on tares in Uptons putting the sheep in after dinner.
Weather. Stormy with bright intervals.

Friday June 24.   Set the two carters to work in Rushetts preparing ground for tares which are put in after breakfast. I help shift some hurdles and pitch a fold first thing and in the morning I cycle to Horsham for some turnip seed. In the afternoon I pitch two folds and dress some of the ewes for foot-rot. Nothing is done to the hay today owing to storms. Mr. Venn and I go to Rookland in the evening after a cow.
Weather. Stormy and cool.

Saturday June 25.   Go down to the farm with the boss and set the men hauling out dung from Honeypool yard on to corner of Uptons, afterwards preparing the ground for turnips in Rushetts. In the afternoon Mr. Venn goes drilling turnips in Rushetts. I pitch forward for Sunday. It is quite a treat to be able to look forward to a fairly easy Sunday with no trefolium to cut.
Weather. Stormy – hay untouched.

Monday June 27.   Up at the usual time and set Moore cutting grass in Ten Acres and Ketchell swath turning in Thistly field. About half past ten we start carrying hay from Thistly field and keep on until eight p.m., clearing about five and a half acres. I go rowing up in the morning and in the afternoon am loading and driving between. Reach home about eight thirty feeling very tired and weary.
Weather. Stormy looking but keeps fine, cool.

Tuesday June 28.   Up at the usual time and set the two carters cultivating in Pond field, Moore with drag harrows and Gumbrell with lift harrow. I see to the sheep before breakfast and set a fold. In the morning I pitch two more folds. In the afternoon I go weeding with Steve in the Gurze. We get ready for hay cart after tea but cannot carry any it being too damp, and wind prevents working of the swath turner.

Weather. Stormy and windy.

Wednesday June 29. Go down to the farm with the boss and set the men to work. About half past eight we start carrying seed hay from Thistly field and we continue throughout the day, clearing it up with twelve load. I am on the rick most of the time and driving between. Do not get home until a quarter to nine. Mr. Venn goes to market with two calves.

Weather. Fine but very windy, making haying rather unpleasant.

Thursday June 30. Moore rolls the tares in Rushetts and then goes on mowing in Burchells. Gumbrell goes cultivating with the lift harrow on Pond field. Ketchell turns the hay in Crab Tree Croft. I see to the sheep before breakfast and pitch a fold. In the afternoon I sharpen two knives for Moore. Mother and Father come over about half past six in the evening.

Weather. Some very heavy storms and windy.

Friday July 1. Time is quickly flying. I start today on the nineteenth month of my apprenticeship. Set the men to work, Moore finishes cutting in Burchells, Gumbrell and Ketchell go ploughing for turnips in Rushetts in the morning. I pitch two folds and crack some cake for the sheep. In the afternoon Moore and Gumbrell go cultivating in Pond field with drag and lift harrows.

Weather. Very heavy storms prevent any hay carrying. Very cold for July.

Saturday July 2. Moore and Gumbrell are cultivating in Pond field and also Ketchell. I see to the sheep before breakfast and pitch a fold and after breakfast dress some of the sheep's feet for foot-rot and pitch another fold. In the afternoon I go kilk pulling with Steve in Hovel field and attend to the sheep again at four o'clock. Ketchell is working ground in Rushetts for turnips in the afternoon.

Weather. Stormy with bright intervals.

Monday July 4. Go down to the farm and set Moore and Ketchell ploughing trefolium ground in Uptons. Gumbrell goes to the station for two ton of linseed cake and two ton of coal. I pitch two folds in the morning and walk round and see the hay. In the afternoon I go shaking out the grass alongside the road and finish with the sheep.

Weather. Fine and rather hot.

Tuesday July 5.   Mr. Venn scours the country to try and borrow a hay-tedder but is unsuccessful. Moore goes harrowing in Pond field, Ketchell harrowing and rolling in Rushetts. Gumbrell finishes cutting Burchells and starts Torrey Mead. I see to the sheep before breakfast and pitch two folds. After breakfast I go hay turning in Crab Tree Croft and after dinner we start carrying it but do not quite finish the field. I am driver between.

Weather. Rather dull but fine, rain at evening.

Wednesday July 6.   Send the two carters to the brickyard twice for four waggon load of tiles, there having been a very heavy rainfall during the night. I turn the sheep out, the folds being very dirty. After breakfast I get ready for market and go over to Rookland for a bull and cow, which George and I drive to market. Have a long waiting job in the market. Mr. Venn has a job to get rid of the bull. Hay untouched.

Weather. Fine.

Thursday July 7.   The two carters go to Pond field but have to return the ground being too wet to work. Today all hands, including carters go turning hay with rakes in Ten Acres and Burchells. Ketchell works down last ploughed trefolium ground. I and the gov. are helping to turn the hay nearly all day.

Weather. Fine, but dull, very unsuitable for hay making.

Friday July 8.   Gumbrell goes to Washington for a waggon load of chalk. Moore and Mr. Venn go drilling turnips on trefolium ground in Uptons, Ketchell harrowing before and after drill. I go hurdle cart in the morning with Moore from Uptons to Lindfield. In the afternoon the carters plough the folded tare gound in Uptons. I pitch the hurdles at Lindfield and drive up the sheep. After tea Mr. Venn and I separate lambs from ewes and turn the ewes over to Rookland.

Weather. Still dull, drizzly showers – no sun for making hay.

Saturday July 9.   Up at the usual time and set the men to working down ground in Pond field. I feed the lambs with cake before breakfast and afterwards go over to Rookland and spend all the morning dressing the ewes' feet. In the afternoon, finding the hay is fit to carry, I rush about after the carters and we start carrying top part of Ten Acres taking up nine load. I am driver between in the afternoon.

Weather. Another dull day and again most unsuitable for hay-making.

Sunday July 10.   In the evening we all drive to Ashington, Mr. Venn is preaching there.

Monday July 11. Go down to the farm and feed the lambs, then go over to Rookland and with George's help milk some of the ewes. Gumbrell goes to the station for two ton of cotton cake. Moore starts on mowing Torrey Mead. Ketchell finishes ploughing tare ground and rolls down turnip ground in Uptons. After dinner we all start hay carrying from Ten Acres and do not knock off till nine o'clock taking up ten load from Ten Acres and four from Burchells. I am driver between. I am very tired by the time I arrive home. I go horse hoeing in the morning.

Weather. Dull till about three o'clock then it comes out quite bright.

Tuesday July 12. Down to the farm with the boss, set Moore and Ketchell rolling and harrowing in Pond field. Gumbrell goes mowing in Pit Meadow at Rookland. I load up some cake and feed the lambs before breakfast, afterwards doing some horse hoeing and dressing for foot-rot. In the afternoon we start on hay cart again clearing up Ten Acres, Crab Tree Croft and part of Burchells. I am sometimes loading and sometimes driving between. Finish up at nine o'clock.

Weather. Rather dull, brightening up towards evening.

Wednesday July 13. Go to Lindfield and feed the lambs then go to Rookland and sharpen two knives for the mower. After breakfast I go to Rookland again and turn the hay alongside the road and rake out around Cart House Meadow. In the afternoon I go horse hoeing in Eight Acres, finishing up the late mangold. Mr. Venn goes to market with a calf.

Weather. Bright and hot.

Thursday July 14. Feed the lambs at Lindfield and sharpen two knives for the mower before breakfast. Afterwards I go to the farm and fetch the side-rake and the governor and myself go to Pit Meadow. I do some shaking out while he rakes the thinnest part. In the afternoon we carry the remaining part of Burchells and turn some of Torrey Mead. In the morning Moore is drag harrowing in Pond field, Gumbrell is mowing in Twelve Acres at Rookland, the other hands couching in Pond field.

Weather. Fine and hot, after a very heavy dew and fog first thing.

Friday July 15. After giving the lambs their cake I go over to Rookland with the other hands and we start carrying hay from Pit Meadow. We have breakfast in the field, then I come back and go on with the tedder in Torrey Mead. After finishing there I go back to Rookland and drive between. We finish there about half past four and then we come back to take up six load from Torrey Mead working till nine. I arrive home about nine fifteen feeling very tired having had a regular day of hurry and bustle.

Weather. Fine.

Saturday July 16.   In the morning I go tedding the remaining hay in Torrey Mead, have early dinner time, then go tedding in Cart House Meadow at Rookland and after finishing this I go swath turning in Twelve Acres. Moore goes to the station in the morning for two ton of super phosphates, Gumbrell finishes cutting Twelve Acres. In the afternoon they are busy carrying from Torrey Mead and Cart House Meadow. Knock off at eight o'clock.
   Weather. Fine.

Monday July 18.   Go down to the farm with the boss and send the two carters, Ketchell and Steve after two waggon load of tiles. I feed the lambs before breakfast and afterwards go binder twine cart up to the attic, cleaning the cooler and sawing wood, then kilk pulling in the maize. In the afternoon Gumbrell goes mowing at Old Barn, other hands kilk pulling in Stock Park.
   Weather. Heavy rain first thing, fine but dull later.

Tuesday July 19.   Up at the usual time. Go to Lindfield and feed the lambs and George having gone off for the day I go to Rookland and see that the stock is alright. After breakfast I go down to the farm and get a horse and go to Rookland swath-turning in Twelve Acres finishing all the field about five thirty. In the evening we take up the rakings in Cart House Meadow and one load from Twelve Acres. Turnips are drilled on tare ground in Uptons today. Gumbrell cutting at Old Barn.
   Weather. Fine and fairly bright.

Wednesday July 20.   Set the three carters ploughing in Rushetts. I crack some cake and carry some to Lindfield for the lambs. The carters come in about nine and shut into the waggons ready to go to Rookland hay carrying, but just as they are starting rain comes on and prevents further progress so they return to their ploughs. I go kilk pulling a good part of today. Mr. Venn goes to market with a calf. We try for the hay again at evening, but rain is again against us.
   Weather. Drizzly rain to finer later.

Thursday July 21.   Feel more like lying in bed than anything else this morning as the rain beats upon the window and a rough wind is blowing, however I make the effort and Mr. Venn and I journey to the farm and send the two carters to Washington for two waggon load of chalk. I see to getting some lambs' cake up before breakfast and afterwards go kilk pulling on Stock Park. In the afternoon I go to Rookland and get the ewes in the cart shed and dress their feet going on after tea till nearly eight. Hay untouched and almost spoilt.
   Weather. Showery and dull.

Friday July 22.   Go to Lindfield and feed the lambs and two calves which have been added to my care. Mr. Venn goes to the farm and sends the two carters to Washington for two waggon load of chalk. Ketchell and Steve go stone cart from Rookland. In the morning I go kilk pulling in the second piece of maize with Johnson. In the afternoon the boss and I go bullock driving at Rookland, separating them, etc.
   Weather. Showery and dull.

Saturday July 23.   Up at the usual time, feed the lambs and then go to Rookland and start tedding the hay. The carters go to Rookland with waggons about nine thirty and after getting up one and a half load a storm comes which stops us. We go over again about half past two and start carrying, continuing till nine o'clock, carry almost all the twelve acres field. I am pitching and loading and get home feeling dead tired.
   Weather. Thunderstorm first thing, finer later.

Monday July 25.   Set the men on store cart from Rookland to the farm. After breakfast I help drive carts from Rookland. In the afternoon the men go carting muck at Honeypool on to the meadow. I help Lucas prepare some nitrate of soda for sowing and crack some cake. This has been a miserable day hardly know what to get up to.
   Weather. Very heavy storms and rough, most unseasonable.

Tuesday July 26.   The three carters go ploughing fallow in Rushetts. After breakfast I go thistle bobbing in Oxons with Johnson. In the afternoon I go to Rookland and dress the ewes with foot-rot. After tea I cycle into Horsham to get a licence for the lambs, have a quick run there and back. Mr. Norman comes up in the afternoon and stays the evening.
   Weather. Very windy but fine.

Wednesday July 27.   Moore and Ketchell set ploughing the fallow in Pond field, Gumbrell cutting grass at Lindfield. I crack some cake before breakfast, and afterwards help load twelve lambs for market, then go to Old Barn and help take up two load of hay. In the afternoon we unload the two waggons and after tea go out after the remaining two load and unload. I go horse-raking in the evening. Mr. Venn goes to market, the lambs fetch £1. 15s. 0d., £1. 16s. 0d. and £1. 14s. 0d. He brings home a drawing room suite. Lucas mowing seed trefolium.
   Weather. Fine.

Thursday July 28.   Go to Lindfield and feed the lambs, now diminished to forty-nine, then rake out round for Gumbrell before breakfast. Moore and Ketchell go ploughing in Pond field. George and Lucas mowing trefolium seed. I go over to Torrey Mead in the morning and turn the rakings. In the

'All hands threshing wheat'

afternoon the carters and the gov. go drilling thousand headed Kale in Rushetts. Steve and I go horse-hoeing swedes in Stock Park. In the evening we take up Torrey Mead rakings and alongside the road.
Weather. Fine, hot and thundery.

Friday July 29. Down to the farm with the boss and send the three carters ploughing in Pond field. In the morning I go over to Rookland and dress the ewes' feet again. In the afternoon Steve and I go horse-hoeing the swedes in Stock Park. The Lucases finish cutting the seed trefolium.
Weather. Fine and fairly bright.

Saturday July 30. Get up at four thirty and with the gov. go to the farm and help turn the trefolium seed, then come back and have something to eat and then I feed the lambs and turn them over to Rookland. The three carters go ploughing in Pond field in the morning and in the afternoon we start carrying the hay at Lindfield. I work until six thirty, then feed the lambs and afterwards get ready to start for home arriving there about eight thirty, having got off till Tuesday morning.
Weather. Fine.

Monday August 1. Trefolium seed is carried today.
Up to eight o'clock breakfast after spending a night with my old mate Sid. After breakfast Father and I drive to Slinfold for a parcel, Sid cycles and I drive home, then we load the trap with Father, Harold, Sid and myself and go for a drive round Christ's Hospital, getting back to dinner, after which I look through the bees, then we have a game of tennis and just before three o'clock Sid starts off to the station in the trap. Harold and I go with him and we drive home round Barnes Green. In the evening Harold and I dig potatoes and go rabbit hunting.
Weather. Lovely.

Tuesday August 2. Get up to a fairly early breakfast and start again for Dial Post about half to eight arriving just after eight thirty. The men finish ploughing in Pond field today, the labourers are hedge trimming. I go thistle cutting with Johnson in the morning and afternoon and at four o'clock go to Rookland and feed the lambs. Lodgings seem so different after a few days at home. No place like Home.
Weather. Very showery.

Wednesday August 3. Up at the usual time and feed the lambs before breakfast. Mr. Venn sets the men on dung cart on to the trefolium seed. I drive between for a little while and then go hay tedding in Nine Corners. Mr. Venn goes quickly to Steyning with the calves and about three thirty we start carrying, continuing until seven o'clock. I am on the tedder nearly all day. The governor is not at all good tempered today.

Weather. Fine.

Thursday August 4.   Go over to Rookland and feed the lambs and trim up some of the ewes before breakfast. The gov. sets the men dung cart again. I go horse raking after breakfast in Nine Corners and then shake up the remaining hay which we start carrying after dinner and just manage to pick it up before the rain comes, thus finishing hay making. The gov. has a rest today so I am foreman.

Weather. Fine morning and afternoon, but a pouring wet evening.

Friday August 5.   Mr. Venn sends the two carters for two waggon load of chalk, the other hands go carting in rubble and chalk to fill up holes in the cow-yard. After breakfast I go trimming back the grass from the corn in Clapper field, another fresh job. It comes in very wet in the afternoon so do not do much except feed the lambs at tea time.

Weather. Fine morning, very wet afternoon.

Saturday August 6.   Mr. Venn sends the two carters to Washington for chalk after breakfast. We pack the wool then Kempshall, Johnson, Abbey, George and I go over to Rookland and dip the ewes first, and then the lambs finishing at one thirty having dipped one hundred and six. I do not do much else in the afternoon besides sending the wool off to the station and feeding the lambs. In the evening I go to Partridge Green for a hair-cut.

Weather. Showery.

Sunday August 7.   Cycle to Partridge Green Mission Hall.

Monday August 8.   Go over to Rookland and feed the lambs. Mr. Venn sets Moore and Ketchell ploughing trefolium ground in Uptons, Gumbrell drag harrowing in Pond field. I go brushing round Clapper field in the morning and in the afternoon finish horse-hoeing the swedes, then go to Rookland and feed the lambs.

Weather. Wonderfully close and muggy.

Tuesday August 9.   Up at the usual time. I cycle to the policeman's, then to the station with a wire[1] and then to Rookland and feed the lambs before breakfast. Mr. Venn sets Moore drag harrowing in Pond field, Gumbrell goes to Rookland for the binder which he is overhauling all day. I go horse hoeing turnips in Uptons in the morning, finishing them in the

1   Telegram.

afternoon, then go to Eight Acres in the late mangold. Ketchell ploughs headlands in Dial Post field in the afternoon, Lucas thatching at Rookland.
Weather. Sultry and rather dull.

Wednesday August 10.   Go over to Rookland to give the lambs their cake. Moore goes drag harrowing in Rushetts, Gumbrell cuts the piece of French Wheat in Carter's field and then goes to Rookland and cuts the second cut clover for hay. We pick out twelve lambs for market before breakfast. In the morning I go horse-hoeing in Eight Acres finishing it in the afternoon and then go to the turnips in Rushetts. Lambs do not sell so well today, average price £1. 12s. 0d.
Weather. Bright and hot, a good start off for harvest.

Thursday August 11.   Mr. Venn goes to the farm and sets Gumbrell on binding wheat in Uptons. Moore goes cutting second cut clover in Lashmers. In the morning I go cake cracking, rake out round for Moore, etc. We have the tackle come for threshing out trefolium seed which we do in the afternoon. I am on the rick helping George. In the evening Kathleen and I go to hear Mr. Charles Spurgeon at Partridge Green and have such a good time, a real treat and feast.
Weather. Fine and hot, A1 for harvesting.

Friday August 12.   Feed the lambs at Rookland before breakfast. Mr. Venn sends the carters for two waggon load of chalk and Ketchell to the station for oats. In the morning I go thistle cutting at Old Barn with Abbey. In the afternoon I go to Rookland and with the governor's help part the in-calf heifers and drive one batch home. Spend a good time at Burgesses in the evening.
Weather. Rather wet first thing, finer later.

Saturday August 13.   Mr. Venn sends the two carters for two waggon load of chalk. In the morning I set the first two folds on the tares in Dial Post field. In the afternoon Ketchell goes cutting thistles with the mowing machine at Old Barn.
Weather. Rather dull but fine.

Sunday August 14.   Go to Partridge Green Mission Hall with Kathleen in the evening, but have a very poor service.

Monday August 15.   Go over to Rookland and feed the lambs and put the ewes on to the tares in Dial Post field before breakfast. Mr. Venn sets Gumbrell binding oats in Oxons but he has to shut out about eleven o'clock, the Knotter going wrong. I fetch a ladder and some feeding pans from Rookland in the morning. In the afternoon Gumbrell and Ketchell are working on the fallows. Moore goes cutting clover in Lashmers. I do a little kilk pulling in the swedes.

Weather. Bright and fairly hot.

Tuesday August 16.   Feed the lambs and pitch a fold before breakfast. Mr. Venn sets Gumbrell binding oats in Oxons which he finishes and then goes to Old Woods. Moore finishes cutting clover in Lashmers. Ketchell turns the lower part. About three thirty we go to Rookland and carry the second cut clover hay. I do not finish until nearly nine o'clock. We have a new Knotter put in the binder today. I do a little horse-hoeing in the morning.

Weather. Fine.

Wednesday August 17.   Up at the usual time. Mr. Venn goes to the farm and sets Gumbrell binding wheat in Old Woods. Moore and Ketchell go over to Rookland and finish carrying and ricking the second cut hay. I pitch a fold and feed the lambs and send eight more to market before breakfast. In the morning I sharpen a knife for the binder and pitch another fold. Rain prevents binding in the afternoon. Moore goes mowing seeds in Thistly field, Gumbrell continues cutting in Old Woods after tea. I rake out round for Moore and see to the sheep in the afternoon. Lambs fetch £1. 11s. 6d. and £1. 12s. 6d.

Weather. Drizzly showers and dull.

Thursday August 18.   Gumbrell binding wheat in Old Woods which he finishes then goes to Carter's field. I have a morning at the ewes for foot-rot. In the afternoon we go carrying second cut clover in Lashmers taking up five load. I pitch two load and attend to ewes and lambs at evening. The Tabernacle go for their Sunday School Treat today.

Weather. Fine morning, dull afternoon.

Friday August 19.   I take an order for a 'Coventry Eagle' bicycle from Mr. Venn.

Mr. Venn sets all hands on dung cart from the mixen to fallow in Rushetts. Gumbrell starts cutting corn in Carter's field about ten o'clock and finishes by two o'clock. I am driving between with the carts in the morning. After dinner Gumbrell goes to Rookland and cuts the wheat and nearly finishes the oats. Kathleen and Grace go away, leaving Mr. and Mrs. Venn and myself.

Weather. Damp first thing, fine after.

Saturday August 20.   Up at the usual time. Mr. Venn sends Gumbrell to finish cutting the oats at Rookland, and then to Tenchford which he has to leave unfinished owing to rain. All other hands are dung cart on to fallow in Rushetts. I set a fold and feed the lambs before breakfast, and in the morning and afternoon drive between with the carts. Manna and Nellie arrive in the afternoon.

Weather. Rather dull, drizzly rain at evening.

Monday August 22. Mr. Venn goes to the farm and sets the men finishing off dung cart on to Rushetts. Gumbrell finishes cutting Tenchford and then goes to the wheat in the Gurze. We start on hay-carrying in Lashmers about eleven o'clock getting two load when a shower of rain stops us. I do my usual shepherding in the morning and help with the hay in the afternoon. In the evening we are carrying wheat from Uptons into Honeypool barn. I am loading and pitching and attend to the flock again at evening.

Weather. Very showery.

Tuesday August 23. Mr. Venn away nearly all day at Haywards Heath market. I go over to Rookland and see to the ewes and lambs and go round and see all the stock before breakfast. Mr. Venn sets Gumbrell cutting oats in the Gurze, other hands finish carrying wheat in Uptons and also carry French wheat and part of Carter's field. In the afternoon we have another try at the hay, get one and a half loads up when rain again comes and gives us a full stop, afterwards we carry another load of wheat.

Weather. Very showery and tantalizing.

Wednesday August 24. Mr. Venn sets Gumbrell binding oats in Clapper field. Moore ploughing for trefolium in Carter's field. About eleven o'clock we start carrying wheat continuing until nearly six o'clock, then we take up five load of hay from Lashmers. The binder breaks down in the morning, so in the afternoon I have to cycle off into Horsham and get a new fitting and come back and set him going again. Mr. Venn goes to Steyning market. Six lambs are taken fetching £1. 18s. 6d. and £1. 17s. 6d. a piece.

Weather. Fine.

Thursday August 25. Up at the usual time, pitch a fold and feed the lambs. Set Gumbrell binding wheat in Long Lanes and Moore and Ketchell finish carrying wheat in Carter's field and start on Old Woods. I attend to the sheep and dress some of their feet and help make a rick bottom in the morning. In the afternoon I go pitching in Old Woods, but we have to leave off about three o'clock owing to a drizzly rain coming on.

Weather. Very showery and damp.

Friday August 26. Mr. Venn sets the carters ploughing for trefolium. George and Lucas thatching wheat rick. In the afternoon the carters go ploughing in Rushetts, landing up for wheat. I walk round and set up fallen shocks and see to the flocks at evening.

Weather. Almost a wet morning, and fine afternoon.

Saturday August 27.   Gumbrell is cutting oats in Short Lanes, other hands
wheat cart from Old Woods. in the morning I am pitching wheat sheaves
with Moore and again in the afternoon. In the evening I am general help
and keep at it till nearly eight, do not get time to pitch tomorrows folds so
there will be no extra half-hour tomorrow morning. We carry the last of
the second cut clover.
   Weather. Fine, windy.

Sunday August 28.   Cycle to Billingshurst in the morning and from there
home. It being a very wet and windy evening I cannot return to Dial Post
so spend a night with my old mate.

Monday August 29.   Get up about six thirty, have some breakfast and start
off for Dial Post, have another breakfast when I arrive and then go round
and do my usual morning's work. I then go to the farm and we winnow
and put up the trefolium seed and send off four sacks in the afternoon. The
carters are ploughing stubble in Carter's field for trefolium. In the
afternoon Mr. Venn and myself drive over some heifers from Rookland.
   Weather. Very stormy, a good deal of mud about.

Tuesday August 30.   Mr. Venn sets Gumbrell binding the wheat in Long
Lanes, Moore cultivating stubble in Carter's field. Other hands fagging in
Crab Tree field. We hire Mr. Hooker's binder and in the evening Moore
and Gumbrell cut the spring wheat in Carter's field and Kempshall and I cut
a road round it in the morning.
   Weather. Very heavy storms, the reappearance of mud makes the farm
look quite winterly.

Wednesday August 31.   Feed the lambs, see to the stock and send off six
lambs for market. Mr. Venn sets Moore and Gumbrell binding oats in Crab
Tree field but they have to leave off about three thirty owing to the oats
being down so they go to Hovel field and make a start on the black oats
there. I am binding sheaves nearly all day and help cut a road round Hovel
field oats. Mr. Venn goes to market, four of the lambs return unsold, two
fetch £1. 10s. 0d. I am feeling very tired tonight. Here endeth the twentieth
month of my apprenticeship – only four more.
   Weather. Fine but not very bright.

Thursday September 1.   Up at the usual time. Go to Rookland, pitch a fold
for the ewes, feed the lambs and see to the stock before breakfast. Mr. Venn
sets Moore and Gumbrell to finish cutting black oats in Hovel field, then
Gumbrell goes to Rookland and cuts the wheat while the other hands go

carting oats from Oxons and part of the wheat from Long Lanes. I am pitching with Moore all day and by bed time feed very tired. Thirty-seven rabbits are killed at Rookland.
Weather. Fine and bright.

Friday September 2. The carters are set working down trefolium ground. About nine o'clock we start carrying oats and wheat at Rookland and finish then with ten load about three o'clock. In the evening we are carrying from Clapper field. I help load for a little while, then come away and see the lambs and pitch another fold. I am dead tired tonight, have had a very hard day.
Weather. Fine and close.

Saturday September 3. Mr. Venn goes to the farm and sets the men corn cart in Clapper field, then they go to Tenchford field which we carry in eight load, I am loading and pitching in intervals. After tea we go carrying in the Gurze taking up four waggon load. All the household have tea at the farm. Grace goes away. Am thankful for another Saturday night.
Weather. Lovely.

Sunday September 4. In the evening I drive Manna to Partridge Green Mission Hall to hear Sister Clara.

Monday September 5. Go down to the farm and set on the work, the governor overlying, then come back and pitch a fold and see the Rookland stock before breakfast. In the morning we finish carrying the white oats in the Gurze and start on the wheat which is all carried by tea time, then we carry spring wheat from Carter's field and then start on the oats in Short Lanes. I am busy loading, pitching off, etc., all day and feel very tired by bed time.
Weather. Rather dull but fine.

Tuesday September 6. I am shifted to the attic for a night or two today. After breakfast Mr. Venn, Manna and I go after six heifers left at Wincaves, then I go to the farm and help on the rick, the men are carrying from Short Lanes, we finish off a rick with this and then carry the wheat from Long Lanes into Lindfield barn. The gov. goes to Sutton to see about his milk contract. I have a very hard day's work moving sheaves, do not finish till eight fifteen.
Weather. Rather dull but fine.

Wednesday September 7. Go down to the ewes and pitch a fold before breakfast. After breakfast I go to Rookland again and we carry the wheat. I am on the rick most of the time, we finish carrying here by tea-time and

afterwards take up a few load from Crab Tree field. Mr. Venn's brother arrives today and occupies my room whilst I go to the attic.
Weather. Fine.

Thursday September 8.   I am rather behind waking this morning so have a scramble to dress. Mr. Venn sets all hands carrying oats from Crab Tree field. I go down to the farm and help on the rick, pitching off and turning sheaves. We get eight load from Crab Tree field, and then carry the black oats from Hovel field. I have another very hard day harvesting.
Weather. Fine.

Friday September 9.   Again late, a quarter to seven before I wake this morning. I pitch a fold and see to the Rookland stock before breakfast. Mr. Venn sends Gumbrell to the station for two ton of cake and Moore and Ketchell go for two waggon load of bricks for the new stalls. I spend the morning at my favourite job, dressing sheep's feet. In the afternoon and evening we carry five load of oats from Crab Tree field. Mr. Venn's brother goes away this morning so I get my room back again.
Weather. Fine.

Saturday September 10.   Mr. Venn sends the two carters for cement, brick rubble, etc. After breakfast I go to the farm and help unload a load of oats and then we go to Thistly field and take up two load of second cut hay before dinner. In the afternoon we take up four more and in the evening carry two and unload four loads. The gov. settles his milk contract with Searle for one hundred and twenty – one hundred and forty galls. a day.
Weather. Lovely, hot.

Monday September 12.   Up at the usual time, go down to the ewes and pitch a fold and see to the Rookland stock before breakfast. Mr. Venn sends Gumbrell to Washington for a waggon load of sand and Moore to the station for two ton of coal. In the morning I help unload the hay and finish oat cart from Crab Tree field and take up one load of loose oats from the Gurze. In the afternoon and evening up till dark am busy about the hay. Finish hay-making today.
Weather. Fine.

Tuesday September 13.   See to the Rookland stock before breakfast, have a hurried breakfast and get off down to Old Barn where they are threshing wheat, my job today being taking off the full sacks from the machine, we finish here just after dinner and then go into the farm and start threshing black oats and continue until nearly seven o'clock, after which I have to pitch a fold by moonlight. I shall be glad when these very busy days are over.

Weather. Fine.

Wednesday September 14. Mr. Venn sets the carters ploughing for wheat in Rushetts. Owing to it being rather damp we are unable to get on with the threshing only knocking out a few wheat rakings in the morning. The gov. goes to market with five calves. The threshing tackle moves over to Rookland in the afternoon and get all ready for a start tomorrow.
Weather. Rain first thing, finer later.

Thursday September 15. Go straight over to Rookland and commence getting ready for threshing which we start about half past seven, starting with the wheat. I am sackman again today taking off forty-five sacks of wheat and forty-nine of oats. Moore and Ketchell have two waggons and carry the corn to the farm. Gumbrell fetches two ton of cotton cake in the morning and in the afternoon goes ploughing in Rushetts. We finish threshing about four o'clock, after which I pitch another fold for the ewes. I am feeling rather weary tonight.
Weather. Fairly fine.

Friday September 16. Up at the usual time. Go to the ewes, pitch a fold and see to the stock. I dress some of the lambs' feet after breakfast and pitch another fold for the ewes. The two carters go to Southwater for two waggon load of bricks and Ketchell for a load of timber. In the afternoon I continue harvesting by carrying eight load of white oats from Hovel field. I am on the rick most of the time and am working up till dark.
Weather. Fine.

Saturday September 17. After breakfast I cycle over to West Grinstead to fetch seventy-six Kent sheep for Rookland which Mr. Venn has taken in to keep until April. In the afternoon Abbey, Ketchell and I go harvest cart in Hovel field carrying and stacking four load. Have to pitch another fold in the evening.
Weather. Cloudy but fine.

Monday September 19. Mr. Venn sets the two carters ploughing for wheat in Rushetts which they finish by dinner time and then go to Pond field. I do not do very much in the morning after attending to the sheep and stock before breakfast. In the afternoon I see to gathering in the last of the harvest by clearing Hovel field, am working up till dark. Mr. Venn is very good tempered this evening.
Weather. Heavy mist first thing, fine and bright later.

Tuesday September 20. I am the only male occupant of the house tonight.
Up at the usual time. Pitch a fold for the ewes and see the Rookland stock

before breakfast. Mr. Venn sets the two carters ploughing for wheat in Pond field. Ketchell ploughing in Carter's field. First thing after breakfast I go with Mr. and Mrs. Venn and Manna to the station and drive back. Mrs. Venn goes away for a day or two and Mr. Venn to Haywards Heath market and is not returning until tomorrow evening. I go horse-hoeing with Steve in Rushetts in the afternoon.

Weather. Fine, cold evening.

Wednesday September 21.   Go down to the farm and set the two carters ploughing in Pond field, Ketchell going after a load of timber. I come back and pitch a fold for the ewes before breakfast, after which I go over to Rookland and see the stock, then back to the farm again and feed the lambs. Then we load up five calves and I start off for market about twelve o'clock Mr. Venn there. After tea I make another fold for the ewes, Burgess comes out and lends me a hand.

Weather. Fine and bright.

Thursday September 22.   Mr. Venn sets the two carters ploughing in Pond field. After breakfast I cycle over to Mr. Looks and bring home thirty-five sheep which the governor bought at Haywards Heath. In the afternoon I drive the lambs over to Rookland and put them in Twelve Acres and then help Mr. Venn shift some of the stock arriving home to tea at six o'clock.

Weather. Fine and bright.

Friday September 23.   Pitch a fold and see to the Rookland stock before breakfast. Mr. Venn sends Gumbrell to the station for manure, Ketchell for timber and Moore ploughing. I visit the various sheep flocks and attend to their feet. In the afternoon I finish hoeing the thousand head and pitch the last fold on the tares in Dial Post field. In the evening I cycle to the station with my bag. Am feeling quite excited at the holiday prospect.

Weather. Fine and bright.

Saturday September 24.   Have a fairly slack day and about eight o'clock set off for Lucerne to commence my week's holiday arriving about nine o'clock. Good to be home once more.

Weather. Fine.

Sunday September 25.   Drive to Billingshurst in the morning with Mother and Father in the new car.[1]

Monday September 26.   Get up to eight o'clock breakfast and about nine o'clock Father and I start off in the trap for Crawley to view Hydehurst

1   Carriage.

farm. We go over the farm with the tenant and also the house, get back to Lucerne about three thirty having got a very good impression of the farm.
Weather. Lovely.

Tuesday September 27. Have a very easy day. Go to Worthing by the three fifteen train, Sid meeting me at the station. Spend the evening together in deck chairs on the end of the pier.
Weather. Fine.

Wednesday September 28. Spend the day in Worthing, seeing friends, walking on the Front, visiting the Library, etc. Catch the seven thirty for Horsham and am met by Father.
Weather. Fine.

Thursday September 29. Get up early and go round and shoot a rabbit, afterwards returning to roost. Later I cycle into Horsham shopping for a few things and then spend a lazy afternoon indoors reading. Mother and Father go to Worthing in the governess cart.
Weather. Unsettled, a little rain in the morning.

Friday September 30. I go round early to try and get a rabbit, but fail to get a shot this morning. I spend the morning printing off photos, etc., and my labours are rewarded by a dinner of baked tomatoes prepared by my vegetarian housekeeper. Mother, Father and Sid arrive back from Worthing soon after seven o'clock.
Weather. Fine and bright.

Saturday October 1. I have a walk round the estate again early to seek a rabbit and after shooting at and missing one I finally secure one. About nine thirty Sid and I start off on bikes for Crawley. We go to Hydehurst farm and look over the farm and house.
Weather. Fine.

Monday October 3. Up at six thirty and start once more for Dial Post, arriving about eight o'clock. I change and have breakfast and then go round and do the bad sheep's feet. Mr. Venn goes to Lucerne about ten o'clock and from there goes with Father to view Hydehurst Farm. Mrs. Venn going with them as far as Lucerne. They do not get back till after eight, Mr. Venn having got a good impression of our farm, and things are looking hopeful.
Weather. Fine and bright.

Tuesday October 4. I have managed to slip back into the Dial Post way and start the day at six o'clock. I go down to the farm and set the men to work by myself, Mr. Venn feeling very tired after yesterday's exertions. The men go dung cart on to oat stubble at Rookland except Moore who ploughs maize piece in Uptons. I go to Rookland and trim the sheep up in the morning. In the afternoon we go dung cart from Honeypool to Hovel field and I help drive between.

Weather. Fine and very close.

Wednesday October 5.   Up at the usual time. Go down to the farm and see about getting some sacks and prongs[1] up for the threshers and until breakfast time I take off the full sacks. After breakfast the governor and I go to Rookland and pick out eight lambs, three tegs[2] and one fat ewe for market. Mr. Venn goes off about eleven o'clock and leaves me to see to the threshing operations. We .finish Lindfield barn by dinner time getting forty-five sacks, then go up and start on Honeypool and by leaving off time get thirty sacks. Lambs fetch £1. 16s. 0d. and £1. 11s. 0d., ewe £2 and tegs £1. 12s. 6d. I have a hard day helping Johnson to carry away the corn.

Weather. Fine and hot.

Thursday October 6.   Set the two carters ploughing in Short Lanes. I go up to Honeypool and help with the threshing and after breakfast help carry away and shoot the corn. We get fifty-four sacks from Honeypool barn and five sacks three bushells of beans. In the afternoon the gov. and I go to a sale near Steyning, and I drive on to Steyning and get the Hydehurst Farm agreement from Burt. The men are dung cart in the afternoon at Honeypool.

Friday October 7.   Casuals mangold pulling.

Set the men on dung cart on to oat stubble in Hovel field. Moore goes to Portslade after an oil engine bought at the Hangleton sale and stays away the night. I help drive between before breakfast and afterwards Goacher and I carry hurdles to Uptons and I pitch the first fold on turnips there and put the ewes in in the afternoon. Mr. Venn goes to a sale at Steyning.

Weather. Fine and very hot.

Saturday October 8.   Go down to the farm and see the sheep then come home and drive Mr. Venn and his brother to the station. Mr. Venn away all day. I am attending to the sheep in the morning and put the two rams with the ewes. In the afternoon I go over to Wyckham farm, Steyning, starting about three o'clock to fetch a milk van bought yesterday and ten churns for neighbours, do not get home until seven o'clock, have a pretty good jaunt.

Weather. Fine.

---

1   Pitchfork.
2   Sheep in their second year.

Monday October 10. Send Moore and Johnson to the station for ten ton of basic slag, five ton each. Gumbrell goes ploughing in Hovel field. I pitch a fold before breakfast and put in the ewes again. The governor is away again all day. I walk round and see the men in the morning and in the afternoon I drive Mrs. Venn and Nellie down to Mrs. Stevens' funeral. Have a wire from Father in the evening about the farm.
Weather. Fine.

Tuesday October 11. Send the three carters to the station for manure, ten ton of slag, and two ton of Fisons. I pitch a fold for the ewes before breakfast and afterwards dress some of their feet and pitch another fold. In the afternoon I fetch the remaining hurdles and troughs from Dial Post field and make another fold. Mr. Venn goes to Haywards Heath market and from there to Steyning where he meets Father and it is agreed between Mr. Merrick and Father that we take over Hydehurst Farm at Xmas.
Weather. Fine until evening when we have heavy rain.

Wednesday October 12. Go down to the farm with Mr. Venn and set the two carters ploughing in Long Lanes. Other hands, including myself go winnowing up seed wheat and moving patent manure. Mr. Venn goes to Steyning market, six lambs are taken and they fetch £1. 14s. 0d. each.
Weather. A wet day, quite a change. Mud begins to be prevalent again.

Thursday October 13. Mr. Venn goes to a horse sale at Godalming early so I go down to the farm by myself and set the two carters ploughing in Long Lanes, all other hands dung spreading. Mr. Look comes over in the morning, so have to show him round and am on the go all the time seeing to the work. In the afternoon I go round again, get home about three thirty and get ready to go to Billingshurst fellowship tea, where I meet Mr. Venn and we drive home together.
Weather. Very heavy rain at times.

Friday October 14. It is pouring rain first thing so the carters stay in until about nine, when it leaves off and they go ploughing in Long Lanes. I do not do very much in the morning except pitch a few hurdles. In the afternoon the gov. and I go over to Rookland and part some calves. Then I go back to the farm and mark the rams. Am feeling very out of sorts with a heavy cold.
Weather. Showery and very dirty underfoot.

Saturday October 15. Set all hands on mangold hauling with six carts from Hovel field to the rick yard. I help drive between before breakfast and also afterwards. 'Tis very dirty travelling but not so bad as last year. George sows part of the late trefolium. Cold much better this evening.

Weather. Fine and rather cold.

Monday October 17.   Up at the usual time and set the three carters ploughing in Long Lanes, Lucas sowing remainder of trefolium seed in Carter's field. I attend to the sheep before breakfast, afterwards I go with the others winnowing black oats. Mr. Venn goes to Horsham in the afternoon to buy a pair of boots. Three calves are sent up today for me to look after. My cold is almost gone and I am feeling much more fit.
   Weather. Very heavy storms with bright intervals.

Tuesday October 18.   I am rather late in waking this morning, so have a rush. All hands on mangold cart from Hovel field. I see to the sheep and help drive between before breakfast. I feed the calves and then help with the mangolds afterwards. In the afternoon George sows about one and a half acres of rye in Carter's field and the gov. harrows it in. I have a chat with Burgess in the evening.
   Weather. Fine till evening when rain comes on.

Wednesday October 19.   I manage to over lie again this morning being about twenty minutes late. The two carters go to Tidey's with thirty quarters of black oats. After breakfast I serve the calves and then the gov. and I go over to Rookland and load up the last of the lambs (eight) and send them to Steyning. I am attending to the sheep most of the day. Mr. Venn goes to market, the lambs sell at £1. 13s. 0d., £1. 10s. 0d. and £1. 3s. 0d. He brings home two pigs. Carters finish ploughing Short Lanes in the afternoon.
   Weather. Stormy and close.

Thursday October 20.   I get up early enough this morning. Set the three carters ploughing bean stubble in Dial Post field. I have to turn the ewes out this morning it being wet and dirty. After breakfast I serve the calves and then drive over to Partridge Green in the milk cart with some corn to be ground. Give Mr. Burgess a lift both ways. In the afternoon I go to Rookland and help George part some heifers and then pitch a fold and put back the ewes.
   Weather. Much colder and fine.

Friday October 21.   All hands on mangold cart. We finish in Hovel field and start on Eight Acres. I see to the sheep, pitch a fold and help drive between before breakfast. After which I feed the three calves and then go down driving again. It is anything but a pleasant job today, so dirty and heavy travelling. I feel today as though I want something special to cheer me up.
   Weather. Fine till evening then very heavy rain comes on.

Saturday October 22.   Go down to the farm with the boss and set all hands on mangold cart from Eight Acres. The sheep being turned out I start on driving between straightaway till breakfast time. After breakfast I feed the three calves and then go on driving between again. It is very tiring getting about today as it is so very muddy and dirty and heavy travelling. Am very thankful that once again it is Saturday night.

Weather. Fairly fine.

Sunday October 23. Cycle to Partridge Green Wesleyan Chapel in the evening, cycling home with Tonie and Donovan.

Monday October 24. Up at the usual time and set all hands on mangold cart from Eight Acres. I help drive between before breakfast. After breakfast I feed the calves and then go driving again. The mangold come in much better today it having dried up nicely yesterday. George and Gumbrell knock off about nine o'clock and go wheat sowing in Rushetts, George sowing and Gumbrell harrowing twice behind.

Weather. Fine and bright.

Tuesday October 25. Go down to the farm with the boss and set all hands on wheat sowing in Pond field. George and Lucas sowing, Gumbrell harrowing after them, Johnson putting on Fisons wheat fertilizer with manure distributor and Steve follows him with the harrows, all the field is sown and harrowed once, but not finished off properly. Moore is taking out water furrows in Rushetts and cross harrows the sown part in the afternoon. I am busy all day.

Weather. Fine, rather dull.

Wednesday October 26. Set the men sowing Rivets wheat in Short Lanes. Lucas sowing seed George sowing Kainite and Johnson drilling super phosphates, Gumbrell harrowing twice. Moore cross-harrows Pond field. I see to the sheep first thing and afterwards feed the calves and go over to Rookland to put the stock to rights. We get a letter from the landlady of Hydehurst Farm to say that she will accept us as tenants of same. Mr. Venn goes to Steyning market and brings back two calves.

Weather. Lovely.

Thursday October 27. Send Gumbrell cross-harrowing in Short Lanes, Moore taking out water furrows in Pond field and Short Lanes. Johnson goes to the station for two ton of Bibby cake. I see to the ewes and pitch a fold before breakfast and afterwards feed my calves. In the afternoon the three carters go ploughing in Dial Post field. Mr. Venn and Father go to Hydehurst today and meet the agent there as all is settled up most satisfactorily, Praise the Lord.

Weather. Fine and rather dull.

Friday October 28.   Go down to the farm and set the two carters ploughing in Seven Acres at Rookland. Johnson putting away machinery into Old Barn. I see to the sheep before breakfast and afterwards feed my calves now increased to five. Then I go to the farm and help winnow thirty-four quarters of wheat in the stores. In the afternoon Johnson goes to Partridge Green station for a water tank. I help winnow and pitch my last fold on the turnips in Uptons. Mr. Venn goes away about twelve o'clock to the Devonshire House meeting and not returning until tomorrow.
    Weather. Showery to fine.

Saturday October 29.   Send the carters to the station with seventeen quarters of wheat. Johnson goes ploughing in Uptons after the sheep. I help load the wheat and set on Johnson before breakfast and afterwards feed the calves, then I go down to the farm again and look around. In the afternoon the carters go to the station with another seventeen quarters of wheat. Tonie comes over to tea and Mr. Venn arrives at a quarter to seven. I am very much disappointed at not being able to accompany her home owing to Mr. Venn wanting to know all the news of the farm.
    Weather. Fine but dull.

Sunday October 30.   Cycle to Partridge Green with Kathleen in the evening.

Monday October 31.   Twenty-two days fine and nine with rain this month.
    Set all hands on mangold cart from Eight Acres. I help drive between before breakfast and afterwards feed the calves and then go down again and help fill. We are at the mangolds again in the afternoon and after four o'clock George and Lucas sow an acre of tares and rye mixed in Long Lanes and I finish harrowing them in and after tea serve the calves again.
    Weather. Fine with cold wind at evening.

Tuesday November 1.   Get up at usual time and find a pouring wet and very rough morning. Send Gumbrell to the station for two ton of coal and Moore puts away the mower and binder into Old Barn and then goes hedge trimming cart. I see to the sheep before breakfast and afterwards attend to the calves. Then George and I drive back a straying heifer from Finches to Rookland and in the afternoon we go winnowing wheat.
    Weather. Almost a wet morning, turning out very fine in the afternoon.

Wednesday November 2.   Set all hands and five carts on mangold cart at Rookland, putting them into the barn. I go over and help before breakfast and afterwards feed the calves, then go down to the farm with the boss and help him measure off one of the mangolders. In the afternoon I go over to Burgesses and order a coat and mack for myself, then go over and help with the mangolds at Rookland. Mr. Venn goes to Steyning market. The household are rather bad-tempered today.

Weather. Fine with cold wind.

Thursday November 3. Mr. Venn unwell, so stays in bed. I send the three carters ploughing in Dial Post field which they finish and then go to Seven Acres at Rookland. I go round and see the sheep before breakfast and afterwards feed the calves. In the afternoon I have to drive over to Partridge Green to see the vet about a sick heifer, have a ride in pouring rain.

Weather. Fine first thing, heavy rain later.

Friday November 4. Father pays a deposit of £100 on Hydehurst Farm today.

Go down to the farm by myself and send Moore and Gumbrell ploughing in Seven Acres at Rookland. Johnson goes to the station for a ton of meal. I see the ewes and then come home to breakfast, after which I feed the calves and then help the gov. bring up a heifer, Spider, to Lindfield and fetch three heifers from Rookland. In the afternoon I dress the ewes' feet. Johnson goes to plough at Rookland. Tonie comes over and I accompany her home in the evening.

Weather. Fine and rather cold.

Saturday November 5. Go down to the farm by myself, the gov. still preferring to rest on in bed. Set the men on mangold cart at Rookland with five carts. We finish hauling there about eleven o'clock, then come back and continue in Eight Acres. I see the sheep and feed the heifers at Lindfield before breakfast, afterwards serving the calves and then go to Rookland and help with the mangold cart. I have the same job in the afternoon. One more week gone.

Weather. A very sharp frost this morning followed by fine, bright day.

Monday November 7. Send the three carters ploughing wheat stubble in Seven Acres at Rookland. I see the sheep before breakfast and feed the heifer at Lindfield. Afterwards I feed the calves and then help the gov. put up some corn for the mill and spend the rest of the morning doing the ewes' feet. In the afternoon I finish the ewes and help Mr. Venn do some bullock driving. The threshing tackle comes in today for action tomorrow.

Weather. Windy, but fine.

Tuesday November 8. Up at the usual time and sent the two carters ploughing at Rookland finishing off Seven Acres and Dial Post field. All other hands are threshing. I attend to the sacks till George comes and then go round and see to the ewes and feed the heifer at Lindfield before breakfast. In the morning and afternoon I am helping Johnson carry the oats up to the granary. We thresh white oats from Hovel field getting one hundred and nineteen sacks.

Weather. Fine and fairly bright.

Wednesday November 9.   Go down to the farm with Mr. Venn and set the two carters ploughing in Uptons. All other hands helping with the threshing. I mind the sacks until George comes and then do the morning feeding. After breakfast I serve the calves and then go over to Rookland and help the gov. load five tegs and three ewes for market. We finish threshing wheat stack from Old Wood by one o'clock getting fifty-three sacks. Very sharp frost this morning.

Weather. Fine, bright and cold.

Thursday November 10.   Set the two carters ploughing in Uptons. Johnson and Abbey go picking up hedge trimmings from Dial Post field. About ten o'clock we all start on mangold cart, a sharp frost preventing an earlier start. I am helping load all the morning. In the afternoon the two Lucases go sowing wheat in Seven Acres at Rookland and the three carters harrowing behind putting in four and a half acres. I receive my new overcoat from Burgess.

Weather. Very cold first thing, rain comes on in the evening.

Friday November 11.   Cows lie in all day.

Send the three carters ploughing yonder side of Hovel field. I see the sheep and feed the heifer at Lindfield before breakfast. Afterwards I feed the calves and then go with George measuring pieces in Hovel and Crab Tree fields which they have fagged. In the afternoon I attend the remaining lame ewes and clean out my calves. Mr. Venn hears of another farm pupil. I write my first letter to Tonie this evening.

Weather. Fine with rough wind.

Saturday November 12.   Up at the usual time and set the carters on hedge-trimming cart for covering mangold pies. Johnson goes to the station for two ton of cotton cake. About half past nine we start carting mangold from Stock Park pieing them in the field. I look round at the ewes before breakfast and afterwards feed the calves, and then help load the mangold. In the afternoon we cart into the farm. I cycle into West Grinstead in the evening to get my withdrawal of £4.

Weather. Fine, sharp frost.

Sunday November 13.   I cycle home and am prevented from returning tonight by rain.

Monday November 14. I get up about six o'clock and make myself a cup of cocoa and about six thirty make another start for Dial Post and after having to go about four miles out of my way owing to floods and having a side-slip arrive about eight o'clock. Mr. Venn and I drive three calves over to Rookland and bring back eleven heifers and shut up six over there in the stable. In the afternoon I go over to Rookland after a water tank for the cows. Carters ploughing in Hovel field.
Weather. Showery and dirty.

Tuesday November 15. Go down to the farm and set the three carters ploughing in Hovel field. I see to the sheep and feed the heifer at Lindfield before breakfast. Afterwards I serve the calves and then go down and clean up the stores ready for winnowing wheat. In the afternoon I help Steve get some hay and straw and finish up after tea by feeding the calves.
Weather. Showery and very dirty getting about.

Wednesday November 16. Set the men gathering up hedge trimmings for mangold pies. I help Moore grease the carts before breakfast. Afterwards I feed the calves and then go down and we all start carting mangold from Stock Park, continuing same through the day. Am feeling very seedy this evening, having got hold of another cold somewhere.
Weather. Fine.

Thursday November 17. Go down to the farm with Mr. Venn and set all hands on mangold cart from Stock Park to the farm. After breakfast I feed the calves and then go down and help with the mangolds, driving between is my job today. Mr. Venn and Kathleen go into Horsham Fat Stock Show and are away nearly all day. I am feeling very heavy and dull today owing to my cold.
Weather. Frosty and fine.

Friday November 18. Do not feel at all like turning out this morning, my cold lies heavy, however I do manage it, and we set all hands on mangold cart from Stock Park, first to the pie, then to the farm. I see the heifers and sheep before breakfast and afterward feed the calves, and then go down driving between for the rest of the day. Mr. Venn is away at the Rent audit. Work seems anything but pleasant again today but am feeling a little better this evening.
Weather. Sharp frost and fine.

Saturday November 19. Set the two carters to finish ploughing for wheat in Uptons. George is sowing wheat in Dial Post field and Johnson harrowing it in. Lucas sows super phosphates and Kainite on turnip and maize ground in Uptons. In the morning I am shifting hedge trimmings and opening waterways in Uptons. In the afternoon I have to go to Chancton Farm for ten sacks of seed wheat and do not get back to tea till after six and then have all my feeding to do after.

Weather. Cold wind and fine.

Monday November 21.   Go down to the farm with the boss and set the carters first thing carting in old thatch to Old Barn yard. About ten o'clock we start on mangold cart again from Stock Park to the farm. Mr. Venn goes off to his brother's by ten twenty-seven leaving me in charge till tomorrow evening. We are mangold cart again in the afternoon, the frost not having given out sufficiently for wheat sowing. I help load and drive between. Johnson fetches a load of timber in the morning.

Weather. Very sharp frost and fine.

Tuesday November 22.   Go down to the farm and set the men dung cart, carting it green out on to Oxons. I see the sheep and feed the heifer at Lindfield before breakfast and afterwards do the calves. Then I go to the farm again and we start on mangold cart, carting to the farm and continuing for the rest of the day. I am helping fill all the time. Mr. Venn returns about seven o'clock, bringing his nephew with him, he seems very pleased with what we have done.

Weather. Very sharp frost and fine.

Wednesday November 23.   Set the men on carting away the various dung heaps on to Oxons. Mr. Venn, Lucas and I winnow some beans and prepare for winnowing wheat before breakfast. Afterwards I feed the calves and then go down and with Lucas, George and Abbey winnow the wheat which takes us till four o'clock getting seventy-one sacks. Mr. Venn is away at Horsham nearly all day about his rates. The carters carry the last fifteen load of mangold in the afternoon, a good job done. Gumbrell goes to the station for two ton of maize gluten.

Weather. Frost first thing, turning to heavy rain in afternoon and evening.

Thursday November 24.   I cycle to the station first thing and order a truck for seventy-one sacks of wheat. Mr. Venn sends the two carters to the station twice, each with the wheat. I see the ewes and feed the heifer at Lindfield before breakfast and afterwards I serve the calves and then have a horse and cart and take some cake, etc., over to Rookland. I do not do much in the afternoon. Johnson is ploughing in Hovel field. Mr. Venn goes with his nephew to look at a farm.

Weather. Damp and dirty.

Friday November 25.   Go down to the farm and send the three carters ploughing in Hovel field. Feed stock before and after breakfast, then Steve and I go picking up hedge trimmings in Dial Post field. Mr. Venn goes off to Brighton in the morning with his nephew to have his teeth seen to and have some out. In the afternoon Johnson is ploughing in Tenchford. I help Steve get up some hay and straw.

Weather. Fine but rather dull.

Saturday November 26. I go to the farm by myself, the gov. not feeling fit after yesterday's experience. Set the three carters ploughing in Tenchford. I see the ewes and heifers before breakfast and feed the calves afterwards. In the morning I do my never ending job of curing foot-rot. I look round Rookland and shift the Kent sheep. The gov. makes me pay the men this evening. I get my new mack from Burgess.

Weather. Raw cold but fine.

Sunday November 27. I drive Kathleen and Mr. Venn's nephew to Partridge Green in the morning. In the evening Mr. Venn's nephew and I walk to Ashington.

Monday November 28. Up at the usual time and set the three carters ploughing in Tenchford field, Lucas and Abbey hedge trimming. After breakfast I drive Mr. Venn to the station and then go spreading about the thatch in Old Barn yard. Father comes over to dinner and seems rather worried about affairs of the farm. In the afternoon I am over at Old Barn again.

Weather. Fine, with cold wind.

Tuesday November 29. Set the three carters ploughing in Tenchford field which they finish by dinner time, and then go to Long Lanes. I see to the ewes and feed the heifer before breakfast and afterwards feed the calves. Most of the morning is spent trying to get up a fallen horse at Rookland. We get him up after a while. In the afternoon Mr. Venn and I go shifting about the stock bringing me up another heifer and calf to Lindfield.

Weather. Fine with sharp frost.

Wednesday November 30. Go down to the farm by myself and set the three carters ploughing in Long Lanes. I see to the heifers, sheep and calves as usual and after breakfast take Lady Bird's calf over to Rookland. In the afternoon Steve and I get a load of hedge trimmings up to Lindfield. Mr. Venn goes to Steyning market with a calf. Moore fetches two ton of cotton cake. Have managed to get to the end of the twenty-third month.

Weather. Almost a wet day, very miserable.

Thursday December 1.   Set the three carters ploughing in Long Lanes. I do my usual morning's work, finishing it as soon as possible and then get ready for a run to Lucerne arriving at about quarter past eleven. Father and I soon start off in the car for Hydehurst, have dinner with Mr. Merrick and settle with him a few questions and agree for possession of the house on January 16th, 1911. I have my first lesson in starting the gas engine, we drive back to Lucerne for tea and I start for Dial Post about half to seven.
    Weather. Dull but fairly fine.

Friday December 2.   Up at the usual time and set Gumbrell and Johnson ploughing in Long Lanes. Moore goes to the station for the grinding mill and cake cracker. I do my usual morning's work and then go down to the farm and sort out sacks and tidy up the stores. I do a few odd jobs in the afternoon. In the evening I cycle over to Looks to fetch Kathleen home.
    Weather. Dull, but fine.

Saturday December 3.   Down to the farm and set the men caddling, getting in swedes for the cowmen and clearing up muck. I do my usual feeding of stock before breakfast and afterwards attend to the calves. Then Mr. Venn and I have a walk over part of the farm. In the afternoon I help get up some hay and straw. The carters finish ploughing in Long Lanes and start in Crab Tree field.
    Weather. Damp and dull, coming on to rain in the evening.

Monday December 5.   Send the two carters ploughing in Crab Tree field. Johnson goes to the station for two ton of coal. I attend to the ewes and heifers before breakfast and afterwards the calves. In the morning I do some foot-rot cure and help Steve load some troughs. In the afternoon I go over to Rookland and help George put up a crib for the heifers in the cart house and finish up with the usual feeding. Heavy floods out at the farm.
    Weather. Fine and rather windy.

Tuesday December 6.   Go down to the farm with the boss and set all hands on dung cart from the cow yard, first on to Oxons and then to wheat stubble in Uptons. I do my usual morning work with ewes, heifers and calves and then drive Mr. Venn to the station, he going to Haywards Heath market. In the afternoon I help drive between with the carts and finish up with the usual feeding.
    Weather. Fairly fine.

Wednesday December 7.   Gumbrell and Johnson go ploughing in Crab Tree field. Moore goes to the timber yard for timber and then to the station for two ton of fattening cake. I go my usual round of seeing to the stock before breakfast and then do the calves and afterwards Steve and I fill up the large

water tank for the new engine. In the afternoon I help Moore unload the cake.
Weather. Fine but dull.

Thursday December 8.   Set the men on wheat sowing in Uptons, George and
Lucas sowing and three harrow teams. I see to the ewes and heifers before
breakfast and then the calves and afterwards take out some wheat for the
sowers, and then go to Partridge Green mill with some wheat. Sowing is
stopped at dinner time owing to rain coming on. In the afternoon George and
I drive four heifers over to Rookland. The new engine starts working today.
Weather. Fine morning, pouring wet afternoon.

Friday December 9.   Up at the usual time and cycle down to see Mr. Thorn
and return to see about my usual work. The gov. sends the carters ploughing
in Crab Tree field. After breakfast I feed e calves and then Mr. Venn and I go
over to Rookland and shift the Kent sheep. I go down to the farm after dinner
and then drive to the station to meet Mr. Venn's nephew who turns up after I
have had an hour's wait. Carters in the stable this afternoon. Abundance of
mud prevails everywhere.
Weather. Fine morning, heavy showers in the afternoon.

Saturday December 10.   I go down to the farm and set Moore and Gumbrell
ploughing in Crab Tree field and Johnson swede cart for the cowmen. Mr.
Venn goes off to Brighton after breakfast so I go with him to the station and
drive back, then go down to the farm again. In the afternoon Moore goes to
the station for two ton of cotton cake. I help Steve get up some hay and then
go to the farm and we work the new mill for the first time, grinding beans
and crushing oats.
Weather. Heavy showers, land getting very sodden.

Sunday December 11.   Kathleen and I drive to Billingshurst in the morning,
Mother and Father being there. In the evening we cycle to Partridge Green
together.

Monday December 12.   Go down to the farm with the boss and send the two
carters to the station for four waggon load of flint and Johnson goes to
Rookland with cake. I do my usual work before breakfast. At breakfast Mr.
Venn and I decide to go to Pulborough market so we start off about ten
o'clock and arrive there just after eleven o'clock the market being all over.
We start back about one o'clock having a ride in pouring rain. Afterwards I
go to the farm and do my evening's work. After tea I change and drive over
to Westlands for Kathleen, the pony going down on the way there but not
hurting herself at all.
Weather. Very heavy rain and tremendous floods.

Tuesday December 13. Up at the usual time and send the two carters to the station twice each for flints. I do my usual feeding before breakfast and afterwards see to the calves. The governor goes to Haywards Heath and Brighton. I go down to the farm and do various jobs in the morning. In the afternoon I go to Rookland and shift the Kent sheep. I do my evening feeding early and drive to the station to fetch Eunice.

Weather. Very windy, but not a great deal of rain.

Wednesday December 14. Go down to the farm by myself and send Moore to the station twice for flints. Gumbrell and Johnson go ploughing in Crab Tree field. I feed the heifers at Old Barn and Lindfield before breakfast and the calves afterwards. In the afternoon I work the new mill, crushing the carters' oats and grinding some meal for the pigs. Mr. Venn goes to Steyning market and Fat Stock Show.

Weather. Fine morning, wet afternoon.

Thursday December 15. Woke up to find the same old sort again, pouring rain and rough wind. I go down to the farm by myself. The men are unable to do anything until it clears up, when they go dung cart from the cow yard to the mixen under the oak tree. I do my usual morning's feeding of heifers and calves and then go down and help drive between. The gov. is very seedy today and does not stir out at all. I help with the carts again in the afternoon and do my usual evening round. I am in the stable with the pony clippers till twelve fifteen a.m. so do not get much beauty sleep.

Friday December 16. Have the same old sort again this morning, pouring and driving rain. I go down to the farm by myself again this morning. The men going dung cart again when weather permits. I feed the heifers at Old Barn and Lindfield before breakfast and afterwards the calves. I do not do very much else except attend to stock in the morning. In the afternoon I help Steve get up some hay for Lindfield.

Saturday December 17. Set the men carting in swedes for the cowmen and afterwards dung cart on to the mixen and out into Oxons. I do my usual stock feeding. In the morning I help drive between with the carts and in the afternoon I go down and crush ten bushels of oats for the horses and finish up with the usual evening's work. Only one week.

Weather. Finer, very little rain.

Monday December 19. Send the three carters ploughing in Crab Tree field. I attend to the stock at Lindfield and Old Barn before breakfast. The threshing machine comes in about nine o'clock so have to do a bit of scuttling about to get ready for threshing which we start about ten o'clock and continue for the rest of the day. I am helping on the straw rick and with the sacks. Mr. Venn goes into Horsham with the girls. We get one hundred and fifteen sacks of white oats off today.

Weather. Except for a little drizzly rain, fine.

Tuesday December 20.   Up at the usual time and send Moore ploughing in Crab Tree field and the other two carters threshing. We finish threshing about ten o'clock getting one hundred and seventy sacks of oats. Afterwards the carters go to plough finishing off Crab Tree field by dinner time. In the afternoon they go dung cart on to Oxons from the lower yard. Mr. Venn and I go measuring mangold ground in the morning and in the afternoon I get up some straw for litter.

Weather. Fine and very mild.

Wednesday December 21.   Go down to the farm with the boss and set the men dung cart from the lower yard to Oxons. I feed the stock at Old Barn and Lindfield. After breakfast I do the calves and then go to the farm and bring up a calf for Mr. Venn to take to market, and then go down again and do some corn grinding till dinner time. In the afternoon George and I go measuring mangold ground in Oxons, Rushetts and Eight Acres. Grace arrives today.

Weather. Rather showery, mild.

Thursday December 22.   Do not go down to the farm but feed at Lindfield straight away and then do the calves and get ready and get to the station in time to meet the nine o'one train to Crawley. I meet Father there and with him and Mr. Smith drive to Hydehurst farm for the valuation which starts about ten o'clock. We get plenty of running about and Mr. Merrick provides us with a good dinner at one o'clock after which the valuing continues up till about seven thirty. Father and I leave about five arriving at Lucerne about six fifteen and I catch the eight fifty-one from West Horsham for West Grinstead.

Weather. Foggy first, bright later.

Friday December 23.   Up at the usual time. Go down to the farm with the boss and send Moore to the station for two ton of maize gluten, Gumbrell shackling and Johnson emptying the cess pool. I feed the stock at Old Barn and Lindfield before breakfast and afterwards do the calves. In the morning George and I go measuring, finishing off the mangold ground. In the afternoon I help George fold up some cloths and Steve to get up some hay and do the usual evening's feeding. Spend a very enjoyable evening with the girls it being Kathleen's birthday.

Weather. Fine and fairly mild.

The Diary of a Victorian Squire

Dearman Birchall

Edited by David Verey

This is the story of a Quaker cloth mer-
chant from Leeds who bought a country
house in Gloucestershire and became inte-
grated with the Victorian squirarchy.
Magistrate, Alderman, and in due course
High Sheriff, Dearman Birchall pursued
the fashionable life, the season in London
and the winter abroad. His brilliant wife's
letters home on their six-month wedding
tour, and later from Moscow and Gibraltar
are outstanding features of the book. We
get fascinating glimpses of their interior
decorator Aldam Heaton, the aesthetic
movement, and their acquaintances Matth-
ew Arnold and Oscar Wilde, as well as the
servant problem, the pleasure of tricycling,
and their country neighbours.

This book provides a delightful insight
into everyday upper class family life in
Victorian times and is edited by the squire's
grandson David Verey who has written
explanatory notes throughout.

256pp   219mm × 157mm Illustrated
ISBN 0 86299 048 3
£5.95 (First paperback edition)

SOVEREIGN

MEN AND THE FIELDS

ADRIAN BELL

Men and the Fields

Adrian Bell

Illustrations by John Nash

The drawings of John Nash perfectly match the country scene as described by Adrian Bell in this highly acclaimed portrait. In chronicling the life of the fields the author, with a sure touch and in beautiful prose, evokes a bygone world of farmers and shepherds, land owners and countrymen.

A new year's eve party in an old farm-house yields a host of memories. As the year's hours grow fewer, the older people do the talking, the younger ones listen, and an England far older than the passing year is resurrected. One old lady tells of how the river was used for bringing chalk and coal to the farms. Another storyteller recalls how they used to go to Christmas parties in the country when he was a child. And so on, through the months of the year – the seasons unfolding in a highly personalised way as man and nature come together in a book to keep and to treasure.

Sovereign
160pp   198mm × 127mm
Illustrated
ISBN 0 86299 136 6 (paper) £4.95

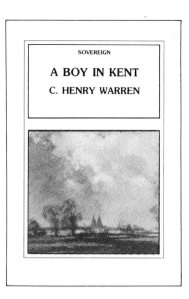

A Boy in Kent

C. Henry Warren

New Introduction by G.R. Warren

C. Henry Warren belongs to that line of writers which includes H.E. Bates, Adrian Bell and John Moore. In *A Boy in Kent* he recreates the countryside of his childhood and his pages sparkle with supreme joy.

> We'll talk of sunshine and of song,
> And summer days, when we were young;
> Sweet childish days, that were as long
> As twenty days are now . . .'

This dedication, quoted from Wordsworth, sets the scene for what is to follow; a world of meadows and fields, the village pub and in particular, the village shop seen through the eyes of a child. Everyone was a neighbour in the village. It is true that the village rambled over several square miles, but all told the population numbered only some eight or nine hundred and it was next to impossible for any one family not to have some kindred feeling about any other family. And the author brings them to life in this vivid and beautiful memoir.

Sovereign
160pp   198mm × 127mm
ISBN 0 86299 137 4 (paper) £4.95

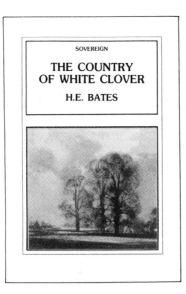

The Country of White Clover

H.E. Bates

In the heat of a clear April morning in the countryside somewhere between Valence and Auxerre, H.E. Bates had the desire, as always at some time every spring, to stop the flow of bursting bud, of fresh shoots, the brilliance and richness and let it rest there. For nothing of later summer could ever in any way, be more beautiful than this. In England more than half the beauty of spring is its length, its long four-month course draws out slowly, uncertainly, with repeated moments of exquisite and infuriating change.

These contrasts suffuse a book overflowing with love for the countryside; a rustic world of trees and flowers, of birds and animals, unfolding seasons and characters such as Messrs. Kimmins and Pimpkins, and where every village contains its Victorian survival, man or woman, who over the years has never made a trip to the nearest town and, in typically stubborn or placid way, never wants to.

Sovereign
192pp   198mm × 127mm
ISBN 0 86299 142 0 (paper) £4.95

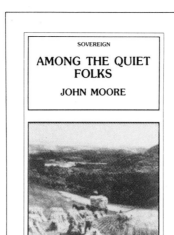

Among the Quiet Folks

John Moore

First publication in the United Kingdom

Here are fourteen stories by the author of the Brensham Trilogy, each of them one of a kind.

There is evocative simplicity in the title story, there is unforgettable malice in the powerful vignette, 'A Cold Wind Blowing.' 'Mr Catesby Brings It Off' is a delectable comic invention and in a boisterous tale entitled 'The Octopus,' four inebriated Frenchmen, survivors of Verdun, get themselves trapped in a wild midnight escapade aboard a carnival ride.

Most of John Moore's books are set in the English countryside but in his short stories he ranged further afield. Whenever he took a trip or a holiday he brought back a tale. 'Tiger, Tiger' originated in Andalusia, 'In Gorgeous Technicolour' on a West Indian island, 'The Octopus' in Normandy and 'Mr Catesby Brings It Off' in the Welsh mountains.

Sovereign
216pp   198mm × 127mm
ISBN 0 86299 146 3 (paper) £4.95

Landscape With Machines
L.T.C. Rolt

L.T.C. Rolt, biographer of our great engineers and author of many books on the history of engineering here tells of his childhood in Chester, on the Welsh border near Hay-on-Wye and in Gloucestershire; of an engineering apprenticeship and career which took him from a farm in the Vale of Evesham to a locomotive works in Stoke-on-Trent and from Dursley to the Wiltshire Downs until he finally settled in a Hampshire village, running a garage which specialised in veteran and vintage cars.

Imbued with the author's love of England and his intense feeling for the beauties of the English countryside the book reveals a landscape populated not only by men but by machines: steam ploughing engines, steam wagons, steam locomotives, canal boats and a variety of unusual motor cars.

With its vivid first-hand descriptions of steam-ploughing, of life in a steam locomotive works, of testing the first British diesel lorry and of Rolt's first voyage in a steam-powered canal boat, this autobiography makes a valuable contribution to engineering history.

Sovereign
256pp   216mm × 138mm Illustrated
ISBN 0 86299 140 4 (paper) £4.95

SOVEREIGN

LANDSCAPE WITH CANALS

L.T.C. ROLT

Landscape With Canals

L.T.C. Rolt

In *Landscape with Machines*, L.T.C. Rolt told the story of his childhood and youth and subsequent training as an engineer. That book ended with the fulfillment of his dream to convert the narrow boat *Cressy* into a floating home in which he could travel the then almost unknown waterways of England and, he hoped, earn his living as a writer. *Landscape with Canals* takes up the story at this point. It tells of voyages through the secret green water-lanes of England and Wales and of the beginning of his writing career with the publication of his celebrated first book, *Narrow Boat*.

The underlying theme of *Landscape with Machines* was the conflict between Rolt's love for the English landscape and his life-long fascination with machines. In this sequel the same conflict is apparent yet we see how it was at least partly resolved. This is the testament of a man who has given literary shape to the history of the Industrial Revolution and who had a unique gift for imparting to others his knowledge, his enthusiasms and his love of life.

Sovereign
192pp   216mm × 138mm
Illustrated
ISBN 0 86299 141 2 (paper) £4.95

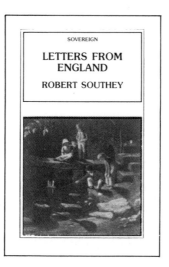

SOVEREIGN

**LETTERS FROM
ENGLAND**

ROBERT SOUTHEY

Letters from England

Robert Southey

Edited with an introduction by
Professor Jack Simmons

Letters from England: by Don Manuel
Alvarez Espriella, translated from the Span-
ish, were published in 1807. Their real
author was, in fact, Robert Southey.

The book was to encapsulate all he knew
and much of what he thought about his
own country and times, and contains a
more accurate picture of English ways at
the very beginning of the nineteenth cen-
tury than exists anywhere else.

The author ranged across every aspect of
English life and his wide knowledge of his
country is apparent from the first page
when he 'arrives' at Falmouth, through his
tours of the Lakes, the manufacturing re-
gions of the Midlands and the North, London, Oxford and a host of 'watering-places'
in all parts of England.

The *Letters* make a book that any one
may enjoy, a vivid and moving picture of
England at one of the greatest moments in
her history.

Sovereign
520pp   198mm × 127mm
ISBN 0 86299 130 7 (paper) £5.95

Notes from an Odd Country

Geoffrey Grigson

Notes from an Odd Country is a celebration of
living and of the natural world and the
response it evokes in man. In particular it is
a celebration of one special place, the
French village which the English writer and
poet Geoffrey Grigson made his second
home. Mr Grigson is a passionate observer
and succeeds in conjuring up for the reader
the essence of the landscape: its trees, flowers and birds, the insects and the antiquities
both historic and prehistoric, the strange
qualities of light and air. In particular he
recreates the people of the region, moving
at a dignified pace through their only half-
modernised archaic way of life.

All who know Mr Grigson's earlier writing will realise with gleeful anticipation that
interspersed with his reflections on the
natural and spiritual worlds are a myriad of
incidental and wickedly funny asides – on
books he has read, on people he has met or
heard of, and on the naked emperors of our
day.

Sovereign
240pp   216mm × 138mm
Illustrated
ISBN 0 86299 122 6 (paper) £4.95